# 1898

## Motherwell Bridge
### *The first hundred years*

# 1998

MOTHERWELL
BRIDGE

1898 - 1998

# Motherwell Bridge

———

## *The first hundred years*

by Terry Houston

MOTHERWELL
BRIDGE

# Contents

Photograph on previous page: Bridge over the Tay.
During 1919 the company completed the Ballathie Viaduct
over the River Tay at Cargill, north of Perth, on the now
closed railway to Aberdeen through Forfar. In this
photograph we can see the steam cranes hooked to their
steam locomotives removing the cast iron arch supports of
the old bridge. The locomotives and cranes are on the new
truss girder bridge built by the company.

Motherwell Bridge *The first hundred years*
Sole Author: Terry Houston

First Edition 1997, Motherwell Bridge Holdings Limited, P.O. Box 4, Logans Road, Motherwell, Scotland ML1 3NP

Designed by Jobling & Young Design Associates Limited, Glasgow.

Printing and binding: M&M Press (1994) Limited. Reproduction: Reproscan Digital Imaging, Glasgow

ISBN 0 9531640 0 4

# FOREWORD

IN anyone's life, 36 years spent in the service of a single company is a long haul. But then Motherwell Bridge has a habit of holding onto its employees. It is a Group in which longevity of service and staff loyalty are valued; when it recruits new talent those brought in very often tend to remain for the duration of their working careers.

In my own case, I arrived in 1960 and remained until my retiral in 1996, in the latter years as Group managing director and from 1989 onwards as chairman, succeeding Alexander Ronald Miller - the "second A.R.," as he was known - whose drive and commercial vision did so much to propel the company to new heights.

Although I relinquished the Group chairmanship in 1996, I was asked by the company to oversee the collation of this history of the Group's first hundred years of trading. Having been around the company for just over one-third of that period, I suppose I was the natural choice. Nevertheless, I feel immensely honoured and privileged to be part of this project.

In my own 36 years I have seen and participated in many of the important developments of the company, helping mould the Group's strategies as it sought out new markets in a variety of fields, the most important perhaps being in the oil and petrochemical industries. I have to say that the years fairly swept past. There was so much variety within the Group's activities, and so many challenges and new horizons to aim for, that there was rarely a dull moment.

Motherwell Bridge, in a lot of ways, is a slightly surprising company. People think they know what it does, but in reality they don't. Appearances can be deceptive. It has moved a long way from its traditional steel fabrication role, growing into a large, multi-discipline international company whose activities today are firmly rooted in innovative engineering. It is a continuous process which could be said to have truly started in the 1960s, the decade when Motherwell Bridge began taking on board the first of many large and important turnkey projects. It was soon to be followed by further company development in information technology and complex control systems.

This company history charts the principal developments and expansions over the last century. For the new and current employee, I hope it provides an interesting and instructive account of those years, giving them a deeper insight into some of the events which have helped form the Group's business ethos. For veteran and retired employees, who contributed so much towards the growth of the company during its numerous phases, I am sure it will bring back many memories. I hope, too, the history will be of interest to our many friends, clients and suppliers around the world. They also have played a large role in the success story that is Motherwell Bridge.

The compilation of this book would not have been possible but for the support of many Motherwell Bridge employees, present and past, who gave freely of their time to provide a wealth of interesting and colourful anecdotal material. The author says help, when asked for from whatever quarter, was instantly, and overwhelmingly, forthcoming; nothing was ever too much trouble. That supportiveness, itself, is very much a practical demonstration of the affection in which Motherwell Bridge is held. There is a genuine keenness to see its history published.

In regard to research, special mention must be made of James Currie, company secretary. As an indefatigable company archivist, he waded through literally tons of ancient documents and correspondence to unearth many of the fascinating facts you will encounter in the following pages, particularly those relating to the company's earlier development. His commitment and enthusiasm have greatly enriched this history.

The first century has come and gone. We approach a new millennium as a Group that is strong, vigorous and prosperous. Today Motherwell Bridge, in the charge of chairman Ian Preston and chief executive John Lumsden, continues to forge ahead with a confidence born of the knowledge that it is currently one of the most successful engineering groups of its kind in the United Kingdom. May the next hundred years be as blessed with fame and good fortune as the first.

**John Crawford**

# What's in a Name?

MOTHERWELL BRIDGE. It is a robust, confident, no-nonsense name. A hundred years ago, when the founders coined it, they were making no concessions to a world which would have been hard put to point out Scotland on the map, far less to a small, but growing, Scottish town in the centre of Lanarkshire. By and large the world was largely ignorant of a county which had blossomed forth as the hub of a Scottish iron and steel industry whose impact was felt across the British Empire and beyond.

But times change.

Some twenty years ago, and not for the first time, members of the Board of Motherwell Bridge debated whether or not to change the company name to something which more fittingly reflected the group's modern day activities. In a way, the name, Motherwell Bridge, appeared to be something of an anachronism.

To be sure, the company headquarters were still on its original site off the Motherwell-Bellshill Road, beside a metal footbridge over the main Glasgow-London railway line; its vast sheds still rang to the sound of heavy to light engineering. But the Group had long since moved out of its original business of making steel bridges.

As a Group, through a mixture of acquisitions and the development of new skills, it had expanded to embrace a wide range of core businesses far beyond its origins.

WEST VIEW OF MOTHERWELL WORKS. Another shot taken in early 1900 of the West view of the Bridge Works as it was between 1898 and 1910. The original office block is to the left hand side of the main fabrication shop with the prominent windows.

In the 1980s it was then, as now, one of the most important engineering groups in Britain; its activities spanned the globe. It had something like 3,000 personnel working for it, servicing industries in a score or so of countries. Its core businesses included a wide range of highly diverse activities encompassing manufacturing, engineering services, distribution, and information systems - the last mentioned making use of ground-breaking hi-tech computer software programmes.

Oil, gas, petrochemicals, food processing, paper mills, pharmaceuticals, the aerospace industry, steel and water - all had sought out Motherwell Bridge for its experience and expertise in engineering, design and construction. In project engineering, it was, and remains, the United Kingdom's leading constructor of storage tanks and gas holders. In the nuclear industry, where once its skills provided key parts of Dounreay and Hunterston power stations, its know-how was again about to be in demand, this time in the field of nuclear decommissioning.

EAST VIEW OF MOTHERWELL WORKS. Photograph taken in early 1900 of the East end of the Bridge Works as it was prior to 1910. In the foreground can be seen the main railway lines from Glasgow to London and the various sidings for the coal, iron and steel industries.

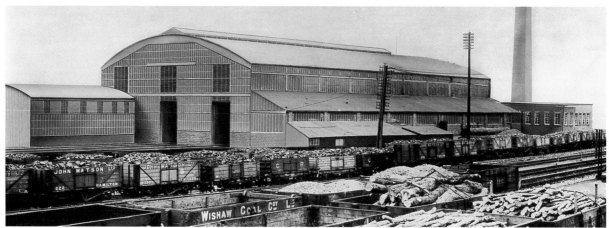

DOCK GATE CAISSON AT LIVERPOOL. Site assembly of a sliding caisson at Gladstone Dock, Liverpool for the Mersey Docks and Harbour Board. At this time, this was the largest caisson in Europe and the company's design was selected in open competition. The total weight of this all-riveted structure was 1,000 tons.

MINUTES AND
MINEWORKINGS. Photograph shows
the earliest entry in the first Minute Book alongside
early layouts of the mine workings around the Motherwell Works.
The various coal levels included Virtuewell, Splint, Blackband,
Humph, Ell, and Pyotshaw.

In project engineering, from Cumbria and the Isle of Grain to Malta, from Paisley to Bilbao, from Germany and Australia to the Middle and Far East, it handled everything from maintenance contracts to turnkey projects. There was not a continent upon which its personnel had not trod. When it came to installing electronic software and hardware packages for monitoring industrial processes, its hi-tech industrial control systems had an international clientele.

Thus in the early eighties, reasoned some of the directors, a name change more in keeping with its modern corporate identity might be in order. There was just one snag. When the Board sat down to examine the notion, they discovered they couldn't do it.

Motherwell Bridge **was** its own corporate identity. Down the decades, to an international clientele, the name had come to symbolise everything that the group stood for:

quality; reliability; experience; high standards of workmanship and service. Some of its foreign customers may still have been a little geographically challenged as to its precise location in Scotland; but for them all the name carried its own guarantee. In that respect, Motherwell Bridge had joined an elite band of world players whose company names, alone, immediately and instantly inspire confidence. Needless to say, the idea of a name change was very sensibly dropped by the Board and Motherwell Bridge has continued to prosper, on its way to achieving its century, not out.

The "not out" bit is important. Scotland has long been the breeding ground of first class engineering skills. Yet the cruel contractions and changes in world markets and a new trading cycle where information technology, rather than heavy engineering, predominates, has reaped a swathe through many of its most famous company names.

# CHAPTER 1

anarkshire, once the very hub of Scottish heavy industry (excluding Glasgow's Clydeside) has but a couple of its most famous engineering names left. The same holds true for much of Scotland and England. An old UK trade association diary kept by John Crawford, immediate past chairman of Motherwell Bridge who has been with the company for 36 years, starkly spells out the decline: Of some 80 firms listed as members in his engineering sector, only about ten remain; the rest have either folded or have been acquired by other organisations - some, indeed, by Motherwell Bridge itself.

To take the analogy one step further. A century ago, at virtually the same time as Motherwell Bridge was being formed, the Colville family of Lanarkshire was only a decade into founding what was to become the world's most famous iron and steel company outside of the Krupp factories in Germany. But the Colvilles steelworks, too, have long disappeared from the industrial scene, another casualty of the times.

Yet Motherwell Bridge continues - and prospers.

The question is: why has it survived when around it so many other famous names from engineering and heavy industry have perished?

The short and probably correct answer is diversification. As a company, Motherwell Bridge has always had at its helm executives who haven't been frightened to grasp the somewhat thorny thistle of change. They haven't always agreed about the direction the company has moved in, either; that would be asking too much of human nature. But, taken in the round, the company has always been

prepared to move forward, using its expertise in one field as a stepping stone into another, reasonably closely related.

Indeed, that is one of the eternal fascinations of business. Whatever the slide rule men may tell us about long-range planning strategy and phased expansion, the truth is that most successful companies do not develop along the straight tramlines of some far-seeing, fixed corporate goal. Rather, they evolve and expand through a mixture of opportunism, good fortune, and, of course, a sound knowledge of their markets. They are driven by the dynamics of adaptability to changing commercial and technological forces, and Motherwell Bridge is no exception.

It was always blessed with the ability to look a little way down the road, note the climate of change, and get into the right areas, usually at the right time. Sometimes it came a little late to the party, but fast responses soon saw it catch up, then excel, as in some of the more esoteric frontiers of new computer technology and research and development of new tough composite materials.

BERMUDA BRIDGE.
A swing span bridge under trial erection at the Motherwell Bridge Works prior to shipment, during 1931 for the Bermuda Traction Company.

It hasn't all been plain sailing, of course. In any company which has traded for one hundred years, there have been lean years, downward world trends and reversals. Sometimes the company has found itself pursuing glittering prospects which have proved to be less than profitable. But the genuine nuggets have far outweighed the occasional fool's gold. And Motherwell Bridge has always learned from its mistakes.

RAVENSCRAIG WATER TOWER. A 1,800,000 litres radial cone elevated water tower erected for the new strip mill at Colville's Ravenscraig development, Motherwell, during 1962. The water tower design was unique in the United Kingdom in terms of such a large storage capacity in a steel construction. Steel water towers were much more prevalent in the United States of America but the relatively few built in the UK have had a long life justifying the original investment.

In some ways, this centenary history of Motherwell Bridge is a kind of extended exploration of the question posed earlier: why has Motherwell Bridge prospered where other famous names, seemingly more than well enough equipped for the fray of international trading, have failed to make it to the millennium?

Hopefully, too, it will capture something of the romance of big business. For make no mistake, trade and industry can be every bit as exciting, every bit as swashbuckling as any other sort of adventure story.

It has its larger than life characters, its odd happenings, its moments of high drama, its days of despair and its days of glory. In a century of evolvement, the Motherwell Bridge story has taken its participants down some pretty interesting and at times unusual by-ways. From the past we learn the lessons for the future.

There is another thing, too, which this centenary aspires towards, and that is to instil in all of us a little of the wonderment about the impact of business upon our daily lives. Scotland is probably no different than most other countries in this regard, but it has never valued highly enough the contribution that industry makes to the fabric of our existence.

In the case of Motherwell Bridge, its impact upon Scottish society has stretched far beyond the environs of its home town as a provider of employment to generations of local families. Like a stone cast into a pond, the ripples of its technology, design and skills spread out, touching

**LEFT: ROBOTIC SAMPLE COLLECTOR.** A remote operated vehicle supplied to Magnox Electric from the company's Elland facility, to assist in a research programme to remove large samples of steel from the decommissioned nuclear reactor at Trawsfyndd power station.

**BELOW: SOYA MAIZE PROCESSING PLANT.** The company project team managed the installation and commissioning of an edible oils processing plant at Taraku, Benu State, Nigeria for Simon Foods Limited, Stockport. The work included a wide range of company skills involving structural steel, process plant, conveyors, storage tanks, piping, water treatment, electrical and instrumentation, and silo facilities. The plant was designed to produce maize, flour, degummed crude vegetable oil, refined vegetable oil and animal feed concentrates. The work started in June 1986 and was completed by June 1987.

GAS HOLDER ZIMBABWE. In 1995 the company erected this three lift spiral guided gas holder at Zesa Power Station in Hwange, Zimbabwe. This gas holder measures 225 feet in diameter and is 170 feet tall when at its maximum capacity of 120,000 cubic metres and stores coke oven gas.

tens of thousands of lives in ways they have never ever thought about or imagined. A few examples: when the trains leaving Glasgow Central thunder over the wide bridge across Argyle Street at a sector known as the Hielan' Man's Umbrella, they do so over a construction built by Motherwell Bridge; for many years when you switched on a light in the West of Scotland, part of the power from the national grid was coming from Hunterston A nuclear power station (now being decommissioned), where Motherwell Bridge made and installed many components and the entire pressure circuits; there is a good chance, too, that the North Sea natural gas coming through your cooker or heating your home has been processed through a Motherwell Bridge designed and installed plant, or stored in a Motherwell Bridge constructed gas holder.

Even the very landmarks dominating town and country often bear the stamp of Motherwell Bridge. Moving back to the company's own home town for a moment, for years one of the most dominant features of the community was Ravenscraig steelworks' giant water tower, created and erected by Motherwell Bridge.

The list is infinite, and far from confined to this country. Motherwell Bridge has impinged upon equally large numbers of lives elsewhere in the UK and abroad. Yet the general public going about its business is barely aware of just how greatly their activities are being facilitated by the skills emanating from the company. Most of us only

regard big companies as being major employers, contributing to the general well-being and prosperity of our localities. The truth is much larger than that - and occasionally we should try and stand back to see the bigger picture.

The Motherwell Bridges of this world are the lode stars of industry which twinkle brightly in the firmament, and we should be mightily glad for their existence. They are the light by which many of us tread a substantial portion of our lives, providing us with careers, working challenges and imbuing us with new skills and new opportunities to prosper. They also provide us with a renewed sense of our own self worth in a society which all too often these days tamely accepts that elements of it are permanently surplus to the requirements of a modern, technological age.

When future historians come to review the latter part of the 20th century, its failure to address properly the exclusion of people from the prospect of purposeful, gainful employment alongside the rest of us will probably be portrayed as one of the greatest errors of the 20th century.

Organisations of the stature of Motherwell Bridge therefore, are of great significance. In a word, they are exceptionally important. But then a century of trading, by any standards, is a noteworthy achievement, deserving of celebration and examination.

So let us begin the story ...

# The League of Gentlemen

The year was 1898. In the drawing-room of Ellenbank, Motherwell, the Lanarkshire home of Alexander Clark King, an engineer, a meeting was being held to put together the financial package needed to create a new limited company, Motherwell Bridge, for "the purpose of manufacturing iron and steel bridges, roofs, girders and work of a kindred nature." The sum they decided upon, to acquire the land and build and equip the works was £19,000 - some £2,000 less than their total working capital of £21,000.

In the event, it was to cost more than that, an extra £5,000 working capital in the form of a bank overdraft, partly because the new company purchased a greater quantity of land than it actually needed for its operations. Even then its founders were laying down a marker for the future. That vision has ensured that a hundred years on Motherwell Bridge still has plenty of room for expansion on its original site, should the need arise.

But let us return to that Saturday business meeting of 1898. The men in the room all knew each other well.

**MOTHERWELL TRAM DEPOT.** Trams undergoing service, cleaning and repair at the Motherwell traction depot. These early versions demonstrate the hardiness of the passengers and staff in the early 1900s with the upper deck and the driver's compartment open to the elements. Within a decade trams were being converted to provide appropriate comfort for the passengers and staff.

They were among the leading business gentry of Old Monklands and Dalziel Parish, a breed of confident, prosperous Victorians who had thrived in the climate of free enterprise and self-reliance which was the creed of the age. Most of them lived within a carriage drive of each other.

They were self-made men all: Alexander Ronald Miller, tall and patrician, a stern taskmaster in his middle fifties who as Ironmaster of the Globe Iron Works first in Coatbridge, then in Motherwell, drove himself as hard as his men; John Marshall, a boilermaker from the same town who ran the Clyde Boiler Works; Robert Park, a Motherwell builder and contractor, who went

**OLD MOTHERWELL TOWN HALL.** The Town Hall at Motherwell Cross in the late 19th Century. Today, all local authority duties have been moved to a new purpose built building called the Civic Centre located at the junction of Windmillhill Street and Airbles Road.

ALEXANDER RONALD MILLER, Ironmaster of the Globe Iron Works was appointed the first chairman of Motherwell Bridge on 13th December 1897. He had served as a Coatbridge councillor and baillie, and later as a Lanarkshire Justice of the Peace. In late January 1901, A. R. Miller at the age of 60 died at his mansion home, Glenlee, Burnbank, near Hamilton.

INSET: JOHN MOTHERWELL ALSTON, a lawyer from Coatbridge, one of the founding shareholders was appointed company secretary at the meeting held on 5th February 1898 to see the company through its incorporation period after which Alexander Clark King became company secretary. John M. Alston was appointed a director in March 1901 following the death of A.R.Miller, and remained on the board until his own death in 1912.

on to be Provost; Coatbridge draughtsman James Campbell Clark; two Motherwell bridgebuilders, John Orr and James Binner; and from Coatbridge a lawyer, John Motherwell Alston. Along with Alexander Clark King, the gentleman hosting the meeting, each had gained the respect of his peers in his own sphere of expertise.

These, the original founders, had been meeting since 13th December the previous year, with a view to creating the new company, and it was now 5th February. They had already selected the first three directors: A.R. Miller, who was also to be chairman; John Marshall and Robert Park. John M. Alston had been appointed company secretary, his legal expertise being needed to set up the company. James Binner was to be works manager; Alexander King manager of the bookkeeping department and John Orr the head of the drawing and estimating department. As salaried employees the last-mentioned three were each to receive an annual salary of £200, plus a bonus of 5 per cent on net profits.

The eight gentlemen had also agreed the extent of their investments: A.R. Miller was putting up £4,000; John Marshall, Robert Park and Alexander King, £3,000 each; James Clark, James Binner, John Orr and John Alston, £2,000 each. Mr Park later was to build the company's first office building, taking shares in lieu of cash. There was soon to be a ninth original shareholder added to their number, William J.L. Cumming, a draughtsman, of East Neuk, Motherwell.

In the King household, they were now finalising the details to create a new commercial venture, the limited company of Motherwell Bridge. Alexander King had already reported back favourably on a suitable site for the new enterprise, a large tract of open countryside on the lands of the Duke of Hamilton, adjoining a tenant farm, and free from the effect of mineral workings in the area - an important consideration in those days.

From the early 1800s, Lanarkshire had been the cradle of Scotland's industrial revolution. Although the site selected was agricultural, it was not exactly a rural setting. Seldom had the centre of a Scottish county been so carved and scarred by industrial development. Coal, ironstone and limestone had always been plentiful; in the 1830s, following the decline of the weaving trades, when the age of iron and steel came into its own, 65 of Scotland's 88 "furnaces of iron" had been established in the Monklands.

One social observer of the times commented wonderingly: "Contrary to what one would imagine, the people are healthy and live long. This warm business seems to be friendly to population. Most of the workmen have numerous families."

Whatever the supposedly aphrodisiac qualities of "warm work" might be, it was a hard life. Youngsters from the age of 10 upwards worked in the iron works. It was a seven days a week process, excepting Gartsherrie and Summerlee, where no work was done on the Sabbath, prompting one Church of Scotland minister to note in the statistical account of his Parish: "The loss of so many days in the year might, at first sight, seem to be a great sacrifice to the respectable and conscientious proprietors of these works, but in reality it is not. The men work with more spirit and effect through the week, with the knowledge of a day's interval from labour before them, and the moral habits are advanced so as to render all concerned better servants and more valuable members of society. When this boon (of Sundays off) is granted, the proprietors also get their choice of the best hands."

That was in the 1830s. When the men who were to found Motherwell Bridge met nearly 70 years on, the work ethos was perhaps a little more enlightened, but not to any marked degree. The character of the county was also much the same. Airdrie and Coatbridge dominated the industrial scene. Indeed, Coatbridge was known as the Iron Burgh. When it had achieved its status of burgh through a private Act of Parliament, its civic leaders had cannily secured for all its ironmasters exemption from the smoke nuisance clauses of the Public Health Acts - with predictable results.

It prompted Robert Baird, a partner in the Gartsherrie Ironworks, to say of Coatbridge district: "There is no worse place out of hell than that neighbourhood."

Indeed, almost right up to the First World War, the smoke and flames that belched out over the Coatbridge main street gave unsuspecting visitors to the town the impression that they had somehow arrived at Dante's Inferno.

But if Coatbridge and Airdrie were the nucleus of Lanarkshire's industrial activity, Motherwell was coming up fast. A mere village of some 726 souls in 1841, its population had doubled, decade on decade, until in the

# Whisky at just over £1.00...per gallon!

WHAT was happening in Motherwell in 1898, the year Motherwell Bridge was founded? The columns of the local paper, the Motherwell Times, give us some clues. The finest Scotch whisky was being sold at one guinea (£1.05) per gallon. Bottles cost 17p. A seven-room villa, with additional servants' quarters and outhouses, and set in spacious grounds in Motherwell was being sold off for £900.

John McAndrew and Co. was selling best Virtuewell coal, Splint coal and Jewel coal and best Drawing-Room soft coal at prices ranging from 35p to 50p per ton - with truck loads of four tons and over attracting special terms. Also available were dross, double-screened dross and riddled nuts at prices ranging from 25p to 30p per ton.

There were a couple of extremely odd stories around that February. A local dentist was stabbed in a hall, and a man arrested. And a Motherwell butcher in Merry Street was complaining he had been expelled from the Butchers' Trades Defence Association because he hired a young girl whose parents were connected with the Co-operative Society.

In a front page advertisement, the butcher said he'd leave it up to the people of Motherwell to judge for themselves. Elsewhere, a local man was holding a Quadrille (a dance) and Motherwell citizens were getting ready to celebrate the diamond jubilee anniversary of Queen Victoria's record reign.

1880s it reached 13,000. Most of the populace were incomers from surrounding localities, drawn by the prospect of work either in the coal mines and iron and steelworks or the numerous industries springing up around them.

The site selected for the Motherwell Bridge works had much to commend it, not least its proximity to the Caledonian Railway (now the route of the main Glasgow-London line), which permitted easy development of rail sidings to bring in the heavy metal plates to be shaped and converted into finished product. After terms had been agreed for the site, The Motherwell Bridge Company Ltd, was officially incorporated as a limited company on 28th February, 1898.

There is around today something of a company legend that, right from the outset, Motherwell Bridge intended to develop foreign markets. If that is so, it is not reflected in the early minutes of the company or in its articles of incorporation. There is brief mention, in May, 1898, of a sub-contract for a Lanarkshire company handling a contract for the Bengal and Nagpur Railway Co., but that is all. However, it cannot have escaped the notice of the founders that there existed bountiful foreign markets.

This was the long and eventful reign of Queen Victoria over a British Empire upon which the sun never set. The writ of Her Majesty's Government stretched to many parts of the world; there were on tap many Government agents who could help smooth the path to a ready-made extended market. Even if the way to foreign trade had not been made a little easier, the industrialists and capitalists would have gone anyway, for they were part of the most confident entrepreneurial era British history has ever known.

The Victorians lived in an age of certainties: They believed that science had solved all the important mysteries of the universe; that all the great industrial inventions had arrived; and that it was their lot in life to prosper from that through diligence, hard work, prudence and self-reliance. Even the architecture of the times reflected that sense of confidence. There was a quality of permanence about it; whether it be a public convenience or a bank frontage, everything was built to last - and last for centuries.

As one of the home countries, well placed to service that vast empire with goods and equipment, Scotland, too, was imbued with the same confidence. For certain, within a matter of years Motherwell Bridge was heavily involved in work abroad on a truly impressive scale.

But before a new company like Motherwell Bridge could run, it first had to walk. Its very first order was in May, 1898, a roof contract for the Lanarkshire Steel Company Ltd. In that first year of trading, there was plenty to be going on with: Lanarkshire was alive with new municipal projects, building up its infrastructure, and most particularly its public transport systems.

Motherwell, as the poor relation of Lanarkshire municipalities, was only a few decades away from employing two runners to pass through the parish with the mails. There was a coach to Edinburgh from Hamilton three times a week; the road from Glasgow to Lanark, by Carluke, had only four miles of prepared carriageway. By contrast, Coatbridge and Airdrie over the same period were already much better served - first by the Monklands and Glasgow Canal, a journey of some two hours to the city (4d (2p) steerage), and by a four times a day train service to Glasgow from Airdrie (8d (3p) for a seat in open carriage; 1s (5p) for an enclosed carriage). The journey took about an hour.

With the arrival of the railway, which passed Motherwell Bridge's newly constructed headquarters, Motherwell was now more in step with the other major Lanarkshire towns. But across the county, indeed the nation, there was still a huge clamour for rail transport. In Lanarkshire, many of the smaller towns and villages had yet to be connected up to the system. In a county which had mass employment, the need to upgrade and add to major public transport networks was considerable. Already the thought of tramcars was a glint in the municipal authorities' eyes and but four years off. Motherwell Bridge was to benefit from that national upsurge of creating a comprehensive rail network across the United Kingdom.

**AERIAL OF WORKS.** An aerial photograph of the Bridge Works taken circa 1957 which clearly shows the considerable use of the railways. The company had its own steam shunter which operated within the works, this was later replaced by a Ruston Hornsby diesel hydraulic shunter which was recently given to the Scottish Railway Preservation Society and today operates as a shunter at the Society's Bo'ness terminal. The then recently completed pickling plant is seen on the right hand side of the photograph and is separate from the main workshops. This plant was used to remove mill scale from steel plates by submersion in a tank of diluted hot sulphuric acid to dissolve the iron oxides. It was then washed in a water tank and finally dipped in a third tank containing phosphoric acid to pacify the process and allow painting operations to commence almost immediately.

In the early months, amid "bread and butter" orders for girders, crane jibs and the like from other engineering companies, one of the most significant contracts offered to it came from the Caledonian Railway Co. to handle the steel work on the Larkhall and Stonehouse extension. It is not recorded whether the company actually took the contract, there being Board reservations about embarking upon such a massive undertaking at such an early juncture. What they most certainly did accept, in those early months, was a contract from the Lanarkshire Steel Company to supply and erect a series of 30 gas producers at its works. The contract for the job was costed at a price of £3,645 - an immense sum in those days. The company's weekly wages bill, which fluctuated dependent on how many workers they had to bring in to handle contracts, was running at the order of £102 to £175.

In the years between 1898 and 1900, the development of Motherwell Bridge was a constant financial juggling act as the directors married together the twin - and often conflicting - needs of creating a fully equipped works and dealing with incoming orders.

The company had, as it were, to hit the deck running.

It was a boom time for business. All around it new engineering businesses were springing up, others were expanding. All needed iron and steel work. But the capitalisation needed to bring Motherwell Bridge up to a fully comprehensive level of operations was considerable.

No-one should under-estimate the magnitude of the task the Board was engaged upon. Unlike modern times when firms walk into newly commissioned buildings, switch on the lights and begin trading, Motherwell Bridge had to undertake every aspect of its development unaided. While operating as a business, and taking in orders, at the same time it was handling not only the construction of its own work shops and the ordering in of machinery ranging from giant presses to cranes, it was also responsible for installing its own electrical power and dynamo-driven cranes; even joining itself up to the local water mains (its first natural water supply having dried up in hot summers) was a Motherwell Bridge responsibility. Notwithstanding the occasional lack of water, a further task was the installation of its own drainage systems to cope with minor flooding and marshy conditions.

All this, while trading and trying to build up a business. The minutes of the early Board meetings, alongside orders for bridges and steel work coming in from the burgeoning railway companies extending track across Scotland, are peppered with discussions on expansion plans.

Capital expenditure was so great that at one point, rather than increase company indebtedness to the bank, with its high rates of interest, the chairman, A.R. Miller, and legal advisor John M. Alston offered to make a joint private, low interest loan to Motherwell Bridge totalling the quite huge sum of £10,000 to fund its activities. There could have been no clearer demonstration of their faith in the company and their determination to see it fulfil its great potential.

In 1899 Motherwell Bridge also increased its capitalisation to £30,000 by issuing 9,000 new shares.

OLD MOTHERWELL.
A 1914 photograph of Brandon Street, Motherwell, with the Royal Hotel on the left and a number 10 tram en route to Wishaw, off-loading passengers. In the foreground is a dray with beer barrels for the Royal Hotel bar.

The financial strains of success were not the only important concerns to affect the company in its opening two years of trading. One of the founders, bridge builder James Binner, left the company, his shares being distributed among the other directors. On the operational side, there were delays in getting delivery of plate on due dates because steel and iron works were so overloaded with work. The consequent problems that created on

OLD AND NEW. Road bridge built by the company in 1932 over the River Clyde between Hamilton and Motherwell, with the old bridge being dismantled.

some contracts occasioned more than a few stiff exchanges with the railway companies, and even lost them business. On the plus side, however, Motherwell Bridge gained two very significant orders: a £9,000 contract for the Paisley and Barrhead railway in Renfrewshire, and one of almost £5,000 to renew the overbridge at Hamilton Central Station. Seen in the context of a total yearly wage bill of between £5,000 and £9,000 for several hundred men, which exactly mirrored those sums, these were huge contracts.

Thus the directors approached the arrival of a new century in a spirit of optimism and satisfaction, and in the second financial year awarded themselves 80 guineas each for their labours, an increase of 30 guineas on their first year's emoluments.

There appeared to be only one, apparently minor, cloud on the horizon as the New Year church bells rang in a new century: the energetic, shrewd and forceful chairman of Motherwell Bridge, A.R. Miller, had missed several Board meetings, confined to his home by severe illness. For what everyone assumed would be a temporary arrangement, Robert Park assumed

chairmanship of Board meetings.

The truth was rather different. Within the year, at the age of 60, A.R. Miller was dead, struck down by an internal malady at his mansion home, Glenlee, in Hamilton, in late January, 1901.

In the death of its first chairman, Motherwell Bridge had lost perhaps its finest asset. The business contacts of A.R., from London to Lanarkshire, were superb. He was equally respected within the municipal world, having served as Coatbridge councillor and baillie, and later as a Lanarkshire Justice of the Peace. All society and business doors were open to him. His presence on the Motherwell Bridge Board gave the new company a level of gravitas it might otherwise not have enjoyed. In commerce, particularly for a fledgling company, business confidence is everything. The loss of A.R. was a major blow.

The company was embarking on a new century, and quite soon, in new directions, in the shape of contracts abroad. Everyone wondered a little about what the future might hold.

# PAST AND PRESENT CHAIRMEN
Chairmen of Motherwell Bridge during the first century include:

Alexander Ronald Miller, 1897 to 1901,

Thomas Ronald Miller, 1918 to 1921 and 1934 to 1958,

Robert Park, 1901 to 1918,

John Alston, 1921 to 1934,

Alexander Ronald Miller CBE, 1958 to 1988,

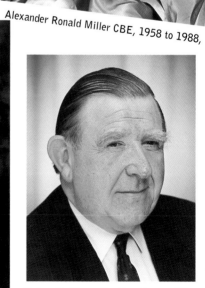

John Cecil Andrew Crawford CBE, 1989 to 1996,

Dr Ian Mathieson Hamilton Preston CBE,
1996 onward

16

# A Challenging Start

For Motherwell Bridge, the new century blew in on the teeth of a great gale which ripped away the roof of its new works. It was a most inauspicious beginning, costing the company in excess of £4,000 to put right. The directors made the best of a bad job, seizing the opportunity to make a number of important structural alterations to the works to prevent any repetition; they also installed better roof ventilation to cope with the large amounts of smoke generated by their industrial processes which had turned the "shop," as it was called, into a highly uncomfortable place for their men to work in.

In the decade unfolding a lot worse was to follow: the company was hit by fire, flood, sudden and tragic deaths, and perhaps the greatest threat that any heavy engineering company could face - subsidence directly affecting its new premises.

Central Lanarkshire was honeycombed with old and new mine workings. While the Board had made a point of being most cautious in the selection of its site, ensuring it was free from mineral workings, it was not immune to what was going on round about it.

Beyond its property no less than eight coal seams were being developed, all of the galleries being at different depths. And many of them were converging on Motherwell Bridge.

The problem arrived almost with mole-like stealth. It did not make itself known until the company had already made a considerable outlay on extending its premises. It had cleared the ground and built a new template shop, and was already well advanced with plans for its new offices, and had just spent a further £2,000 creating a new extension to its works, when ominous signs of subsidence were discovered.

The ground movement also affected proper drainage of

MINE WORKINGS. These mine workings at North Motherwell Colliery and Motherwell Colliery were in close proximity to the Motherwell Bridge Works and were among many mine workings in the surrounding area.

CHAPTER 3

the site. In 1907 the Board learned that the buildings were being badly affected by underground workings. The brick walls of the new template shop had cracked in several places, some of the columns of the main building were considerably out of plumb and - worst news of all - experts consulted were of the opinion that the subsidence would continue for the next ten years. The seams being worked principally concerned the Virtuewell coal seams, which were closest to the works, and seams being developed from Parkneuk Colliery by the Glasgow Iron & Steel Company.

Immediately the company began to cast around for a solution. The best they could come up with was a decision to buy out the mineral rights of the site from the Duke of Hamilton and the coal-mining firms whose activities were threatening to bring the works tumbling down about their ears.

But it was a protracted affair which tainted the company's business trading for six miserable years. The company was caught in a dilemma: while it could effect necessary running repairs, it could not do the job properly until it knew for certain the ground was going to settle. Equally, it was going to cost the firm a pretty penny to buy out the mineral rights and stop the seams being mined beneath them. To "leave the coal unwrought," as the lawyers put it, was going to be exceptionally expensive. In fact, when the deal was finally completed in 1913, it cost the company £6,500, defrayed over a period of eight years. The running repairs it was forced to carry out to combat subsidence over the period of 1907-13 was of an even higher order. In the event, within a year of mining operations ceasing, the ground settled and the company was able to pursue its activities with greater peace of mind. However, right into the 1920s it had to take account of ground subsidence whenever it embarked upon any works extensions, and it was required to expend considerable energy, not to mention sums of money, righting problems.

But there were other unexpected outlays, too, in that first decade or so of the new century. In the midst of the "subsidence years" a serious fire destroyed part of the works roof (a not uncommon industrial mishap of the times because of the large amounts of naked flames in use). The company's workforce fortunately escaped unscathed, as did its machinery. It was also able to

recover the full insurance on the damage. However, its problems were far from ended. A nervous bank, which had probably got wind of the long-running problem of mining subsidence, told the directors it wanted much greater security against its overdraft. There was a hasty move to reduce the company's indebtedness, and new tranches of shares were issued to directors in lieu of repayment of private loans to the company.

The whole six-year period was one fraught with financial anxiety. Indeed, it was during it that for the first time Motherwell Bridge failed to return a dividend to shareholders. They were to make good that omission in the year that followed, with generous dividends, but the "subsidence years" were ones that the company was very glad to put behind it.

There were other reasons, too. Over the years, the company had lost two of its most stalwart founder members in unexpectedly sudden deaths, first its chairman, A.R. Miller, then lawyer John M. Alston, who had been brought onto the Board as a director, following A.R.'s death. The entrepreneurial lawyer, who had missed barely a single meeting of the company since its incorporation, died in 1912. His death was a big loss. In the early years of the company's growth his unswerving financial commitment to the business had been an important factor. Oddly, his will, which he drew up himself, reputedly required Counsel's opinion to interpret - perhaps underlining the wisdom of the robust legal maxim that "a lawyer who represents himself has a fool for a client."

There was another, more tragic death, as well. In 1907, Alexander Miller, co-proprietor of the Globe Iron Works, and son of A.R. Miller, was out cycling with his younger brother, Jackie, when, outside Hamilton Palace, his front wheel hit a stone. He was hurled over the handlebars and landed on his head. Seemingly unhurt, he straightened up the handlebars of his racing bike and cycled as far as the Globe Iron Works in Motherwell, only to complain of a blinding headache. A cab was summoned and he was taken home to Glenlee, in Hamilton, and a doctor sent for. He immediately called for a specialist, a professor from Glasgow. But within 15 minutes of his arrival, Alexander had died from internal head injuries. He was just 27 years of age.

The death was doubly tragic in that only months earlier Alexander had returned safely from 16 months' active

# A Case of Nagging Letters

ENGINEER Alexander C. King, one of the original founders of Motherwell Bridge, aspired to the hunting, shooting, fishing set. However, the grand country life had its problems, as the following letters show.

In 1906 he wrote angrily to a Newmains, Wishaw, farmer, about the fodder supplied for his horses:

"I have examined the cart of hay which you sent down this week, and I am very much annoyed that you should send stuff of this kind to me. You are perfectly aware that the hay which you are storing for me is two years old, and was well got at the time, whereas the stuff that you have sent is this season's hay, and of the poorest description - so poor in fact that Mr Pollock, Veterinary Surgeon, who examined it yesterday said that it wasn't fit for cattle to eat, let alone horses.

"I am vexed to think that you should attempt to take advantage of me in this manner after having paid you for the hay at the time it was put up in the stack ... Either send me the two-year-old hay that was stored under my sheet or return me the money that I paid you for it".

A few years later he was writing to an auctioneering company in Crewe, over the private sale of his brown mare - "quiet in every way, going in saddle, single and double harness". The animal, bought by a Mr Hollinshead, had fallen and hurt its forelegs on the way home from the mart.

King wrote:
"I would make no objection to taking her back provided she was returned in the same good condition in which no doubt you sold her.

Mr Hollinshead has apparently taken her home in a careless manner. To trot the mare behind a trap was not a proper way to use her".

The complaint notwithstanding, he was forced to sell the mare at a knock-down price.

Despite shooting on estates, King was definitely no sportsman. Eager to impress "my friend Colville" (of the Colvilles steel family) and give him a very good day's shooting over Lord Lamington's Lanarkshire estate, he employed extra beaters at his own expense to raise the grouse. He also suggested to the gamekeeper that he might 'paraffin' some of the rabbit burrows on the hillside "to cause them to lie out and give us better sport along the hill face in the afternoon".

What a bounder!

service in South Africa's Boer War with the Volunteer Company of the Scottish Rifles. A crack shot and highly popular with his service friends, he had been so eager to see action that, unable to gain a posting as an officer, he had enrolled as a private. During his South Africa service, he rose to the rank of lieutenant. He was given a semi-military funeral.

It was one of life's ironies that few of the dynasty which A.R. Miller founded - he had five sons and two daughters - survived to inherit the fruits of his labours. Of his sons who had followed him into the iron and steel business, only one, Thomas R. Miller, who joined the Motherwell Bridge Board in 1908, lived to make a true impact upon the company's development.

William Black Miller, who was to die at the age of 43 in 1916, joined the Motherwell Bridge Board of directors in 1902, after his father's death, but after a few years took no active directorial role in the company's affairs, that role being taken by T.R. Miller. Alexander died tragically in 1907 in the cycle accident; another brother, James, died in 1910, aged 39, and John Kingsley Miller was killed in action in 1918, at the age of 34. One of the two daughters, Catherine, also died while in her thirties.

In truth, A.R. Miller had not really equipped any of his family for the task of running a major business concern. A stern disciplinarian and Christian fundamentalist, he failed to give any of them senior management roles within the Globe Iron Works, which he still owned outright.

T.R. Miller, in his book, The Monklands Tradition, says: "Although my three older brothers had been trained and employed in the business for many years, my father had not promoted them to a managership or position of responsibility. My mother had long argued against this extreme policy, but father seemed to fear that early promotion might go to their heads. When he was young

he had seen this happen to several of his friends."

Upon A.R.'s unexpected death, the strains immediately became apparent. The autocratic founder had set up a trust for his family, offering the sons the option of buying over the Globe from the estate, but they elected to keep it as a trust investment, under their management, taking a salary.

From the very start of that arrangement, there were deep family divisions. In T.R Miller's words, his brothers James and William did not pull together. For eight years there was a marked lack of co-operation between them.

T.R., however, busied himself learning the business, because he realised that, unless he acquired expertise, management control of the Globe would pass elsewhere. In 1907, the year before he joined the Motherwell Bridge Board, T.R. Miller took over the running of the works, with some very considerable success in the early years. But the times were beginning to change. The boom years of wrought ironwork - one of the Globe's activities - were being replaced by steel. Technology was advancing, and prices tumbling. The large number of small iron and steel works in Lanarkshire, to keep their furnaces in production, were breaking away from fixed trade pricing agreements; it was rapidly degenerating into a case of survival of the fittest. It was also clearly apparent that unless these small works banded together a lot of them were going to go out of business. T.R. Miller was instrumental in bringing about an amalgamation of 13 firms into the Scottish Iron and Steel Co. Ltd - his own Globe Works being one of that number. A merger of so many firms was a highly complex matter, and not just financially. It called for putting out to grass a lot of active and ruggedly individualist iron and steel works executives who were surplus to the new super-company's needs. But the task was accomplished between 1912 and 1913.

# Inside Story of the Railway Pillars

WHEN Motherwell Bridge constructed vast sections of Glasgow Central Station at the turn of the century, including the bridge over Argyle Street known as the Hielan' Man's Umbrella, welding was unknown. Fabrications were held together by rivets. In addition to holding structures in place, the rivets were also used as a form of ornamentation on the giant pillars reaching up to the huge glass and steel roof canopy above the concourse and platforms. Riveting squads worked in three-man teams - the heater (who made rivets red-hot in a small portable furnace), the catcher or picker-up, who was usually a young boy of 14 or 15, and the riveter.

On the Central Station contract, to achieve the required almost Art Deco finish to the pillars, it is said the catchers were lowered down the inside of the pillars. They would catch in a bucket the red-hot rivets dropped down, and ram them through the holes, at which point, as they held them in place, the riveter would hammer the pliant metal into position.

Riveting squads in most yards could be a source of friction, particularly if the men were on piece-work. There was an art in ensuring that the right number of rivets were reaching the proper temperatures just in time for use, and a clumsy catcher could slow down the pace of a job. With red and white hot pieces of metal flying around, the scope for trouble was considerable.

Back in 1928, an irate father complained to Motherwell Bridge directors that his son - "admitted to be the smartest picker-up in the work" - had been kicked and struck by the riveter he served. He also complained the lad had been "diddled" out of a rise after his first full year of employment - having been told that he would have to serve 26 months with the company before qualifying for a raise.

Welding started to replace riveting in the mid-thirties. In 1936, the company sent one of its key staff to Chicago to study the latest electrical welding methods being used by Chicago Bridge. The following year plans were made to introduce the first custom-built welding bay at Motherwell.

CENTRAL STATION. An early photograph showing the arches over the vehicle carriageway and platforms at Glasgow's Central Station. The giant pillars reaching up to the huge glass and steel roof canopy are to the right hand side of the print. The hansom cabs line either side of the roadway in the upper level.

MAIN PICTURE: GLASGOW CENTRAL STATION EXTENSION. Workmen overplating between the main load bearing beams which will support the rail track. To the right is girder work forming the side of the platform which is also part of the load bearing structure.

INSET: GLASGOW CENTRAL STATION EXTENSION. A view looking towards the Hope Street side of Central Station with a sign indicating the low level entrance.

INSET: CENTRAL STATION PLATFORMS. A view taken from the carriageway showing the support columns on platforms nine and ten.

Motherwell Bridge, being in heavy engineering, was not caught up in the back-draft of these manoeuvres. In some ways it benefited from them - on pricing and in better quality steel. Indeed, as far back as 1902, the Motherwell Bridge minutes talk approvingly of the new steel being used in the shop giving great satisfaction, the results being obtained "realising all expectations." Good news, indeed, but less so for the workforce. The steel being easier for the men to work, the management promptly cut the piece work rates!

It was a logical, if not necessarily popular, decision which had the Victorian work ethic stamped all over it.

Again, in the first 13 years of the new century, there is no indication that Motherwell Bridge was heavily involved in foreign bridge building. Its outside squads were working across mainland Britain - and, on occasion, Ireland - on bridge contracts. There is mention of an Indian contract, and one for Port Elizabeth, South Africa, but the company's single biggest job concerned Glasgow Central Station, where it

HIELAN' MAN'S UMBRELLA. In 1901 the company was charged with its single biggest job. At Glasgow's Central Station it was called upon to provide an extension from the Caledonian railway hotel to Argyle Street. Part of the contract which lasted more than three years entailed the widening of the famous broad steel rail bridge across Argyle Street, which became known as the Hielan' Man's Umbrella.

CHAPTER 3

was called upon to provide an extension from the Caledonian's railway hotel to Argyle Street in 1901. The contract was a massive one, proliferating into a variety of improvements lasting more than three years. Part of it entailed Motherwell Bridge constructing the famous broad iron rail bridge across Argyle Street which gave rise to the street below it being called The Hielan' Man's Umbrella. The nickname probably stemmed from the many old music hall jokes about the meanness of Highlanders compared to Glasgow keelies.

The inference was that Highlanders would shelter beneath the bridge from the rain, rather than spend a few bawbees purchasing a bonnet or an umbrella.

There were two other important developments in the early 1900s. In 1908, Motherwell Bridge opened a London office at 23E Grosvenor Mansions, in Victoria Street, Westminster, putting its chief draughtsman, I.M. Hunter, in charge of it. It also joined the newly formed United Kingdom association of bridge builders. Both were key planks in its ability to tender for the contracts abroad which were to be such a mainstay of its activities in later decades.

But all that lay in the future. In Britain a new man-made calamity was about to engulf the world - the "war to end all wars", World War I.

KITCHENER'S APPEAL. During the First World War many posters were designed with the theme of appealing to the nation's loyalty. One in particular utilised a photograph of Lord Kitchener imploring you to join-up.

# Carrying the Banner

DESPITE the "Upstairs, Downstairs" class distinctions of the early 1900s, there was a great spirit of camaraderie within the works and an active social life. Works outings, organised by the staff themselves, regularly took place, with bus runs, trips and dances. For special events, the workers would parade through the streets of Motherwell, headed by a band, and standard-bearers carrying the works banner, very much like the old "Wakes Weeks" held by mill and factory workers in England. One wonders where they got the energy from: a working day in the 1900s was 6.15 am to 5.30pm.

# Tea-riffic Replies

IN the early days of the Bridge Works tea breaks were not permitted. However, the shop floor wasn't above organising the occasional fly cuppa for itself. One day works manager James Cowan caught an apprentice making his way back to his work place with a billy can. "Whose tea is that lad?" he demanded.

"Lipton's, sir," said the lad meekly - Lipton being the famous grocery chain. History doesn't record what happened to the apprentice. But he should have gone far.

Like all works, Motherwell Bridge had its fair share of wags. There once was a welder called van Gogh who was receiving extremely intricate instructions from his foreman about the job he was about to carry out, when he stopped him in his tracks by protesting: "Just a minute, boss. The name is Bobby van Gogh, no' Vincent!"

# I Suppose a Rise is Out of the Question?

GIVEN the Victorian era's reputation for strait-laced behaviour and over-powering politeness, it is surprising to discover that back in 1900, management labour relations at Motherwell Bridge were conducted with a little more vigour than most of us might have suspected. Managing director Alexander "Paddy" King could be quite hot-tempered when occasion demanded.

Following a disagreement with the then works manager of Motherwell Bridge, a certain Mr Purves, watched by jeering and catcalling workers, he seized the unfortunate man by the neck of his shirt and the scruff of his pants, and physically ran him off the premises and told him he was fired. A great roar went up at the news, the loudest cheers coming from the young boys in the yard, because Mr Purves was not a popular figure.

However, Paddy King got his own "come-uppance" some years later. In 1915, arriving at Motherwell Station, he brushed past a small railway boy "who has been objectionable on more than one occasion and who knows me perfectly well" without showing him his season ticket.

Two ticket collectors rushed up the stair after him and seized King "violently" by the coat collar.

In a complaint to the Caledonian Railway Company's general manager, King, a season ticket holder of 25 years' standing, said the incident had "put him to public affront" and had damaged his clothing. He demanded a written apology from the two men - and that they be fined at least £1 by the railway company for their behaviour.

# For King and Country

"WAR! WAR! WAR! A Straight Question for all Healthy Men, Can you shoot? ... If not, then join at once the Motherwell Civilian Rifle Club. We have trained and experienced men who will be delighted to learn you how to shoot and shoot accurately. Rifles for practice free (small charge made for ammunition) ...". The advertisement emblazoned across the columns of the local weekly newspaper, the Motherwell Times, in 1914 encapsulated the mood of Lanarkshire to the outbreak of World War I.

What the advertisement lacked in grammatical rectitude, it more than made up for in enthusiasm and patriotic fervour. The muddy hells of Passchendaele and Flanders had not yet reaped their cruel harvest; it was all new and strangely exciting - once Motherwell had got over its initial stage-fright. In common with the rest of Britain, the day war was announced housewives cleared the shelves of the town's grocery shops of commodities such as sugar, flour and butter, sending prices soaring.

Three days after the outbreak of war, the Motherwell Times reported: "One prominent provision merchant sold a three weeks supply of flour in one day - a fact which illustrates the 'panicky' state of affairs."

In a 'chin up' note of optimism, the article added: "Altogether, however, it may safely be assumed that while we will pay a little more for various provisions there is no reason to anticipate famine prices, and certainly no reason to panic."

Indeed, the local chronicler was most accurate in his prediction. It was not until 1917, when German U-boats patrolling the Atlantic torpedoed immense tonnages of merchant shipping, that food shortages began to bite and rationing was introduced. But that lay in the future.

**MAIN PHOTO: ADMIRALTY WORKSHOP INTERIOR.** Interior of the Admiralty engineering workshop showing the belt driven machinery used during that era within one of the many bays. Shops such as this were built at Rosyth, near Edinburgh, and Invergordon, near Inverness.

**INSET: WORKSHOPS, ROSYTH.** Exterior view of engineering shop buildings contracted to the company by the Admiralty. The building of this workshop was carried out by the company in its entirety and included concrete work, brickwork, joinery, wood-block flooring, glazier and plumber work in addition to the steelwork. The company also constructed other large workshop buildings similar in design at this base and at Port Edgar on the south bank of the Forth opposite Rosyth.

Back in 1914, London's Whitehall mandarins had but one objective: to turn the United Kingdom into a giant island factory, supporting the war effort. Keeping logistical supply lines open to its fighting forces was the key to victory. Fuel depots, hangars, aircraft, machine parts, guns, munitions, ordnance and a wide variety of material were going to be required in vast and continuous amounts. Central Lanarkshire, because of its preponderance of steel, coal and engineering industries, was very quickly one of the United Kingdom's key areas involved in the war effort.

Motherwell Bridge was no exception.

From the very outset it was deeply involved in war work. At the works it made pressings of copper shell bands, machined caterpillar tracks and ball pivots for armoured cars, machine-tooled spherical gun parts, did pressings for bullet-proof shelters, machined bars for gun parts and mountings for the six-round heavy calibre Hotchkiss gun, did pressings for trench warfare and also the pressings for sinkers, the weights used to conceal mines beneath the sea's surface.

Munitions were far from being its only activity. The pressing need in the early war years was for fuel storage tanks and depots, and the fast erection of specialist workshops, depots and factories. Outside squads from Motherwell Bridge were extensively employed by the Admiralty in war work. In 1914 the company made and erected ten massive oil tanks at Rosyth and a further five at Invergordon. The following year it was called back to install a further three fuel tanks at Rosyth.

**ALLIED TANK.** One of the allied tanks going into action in France.

**SOLDIERS ON THE MOVE.** The war years depleted many workshops. Vast numbers of service personnel were required during the Great War years. Although there was the system of reserved occupations many in this category volunteered for active service.

**FEMALE WORKERS.** To meet the labour demands during these trying early years of the First World War female workers filled the gaps created by men volunteering for active service. They were very much involved in making ammunition shells, operating a wide variety of machines, and working on the land.

**ADMIRALTY TANKAGE.** 117 feet diameter storage tanks constructed for the Admiralty at an oil fuel depot. During World War I, depots were built by the company at many locations throughout the UK, including Bowling on the River Clyde, Rosyth, and Invergordon. After the war further storage depots were built at Devonport in the UK and overseas at Rangoon, Aden, Trincomali, Singapore and Sierra Leone. This investment resulted from Churchill's decision early in World War I when he was First Lord of the Admiralty to convert the British Navy from coal to oil fuel.

# Send Gunboats Please

AFFRONTED civic pride is a terrible thing to behold. There was great rivalry between Motherwell Burgh Council and Lanarkshire County Council over their separate municipal water supplies and in 1918, towards the tail-end of the First World War, consumers were still being jealously fought over by the two authorities. Motherwell Bridge was connected to both mains. Much to the chagrin of Lanarkshire County Council, the company insisted on using Motherwell Burgh water for its boilers because there was too high a lime-scale content in County supplies. However, the

County demanded an end to the anomaly of the double connection and instructed the Burgh Engineer to disconnect the Motherwell supply.

To the pugnacious managing director, A.C. King, that was fighting talk. He fired a shot across the District Water Works Engineer's bows, warning him that the company was engaged on Admiralty work "of the very highest possible priority" and that any disconnection would "incur a very grave responsibility."

The battle of wits continued, with King constantly raising the stakes. In a letter to the Motherwell Burgh Surveyor, who

seemed inclined to disconnect the Motherwell Burgh supply, he wrote: "We have already informed you that we are engaged on Admiralty contracts of the very highest priority, one in particular which has to do with Cross Channel Communications to France, the completion of which must not be hindered for a single moment ... if you take the drastic step of cutting off our water supply, you will personally be liable to have a very serious charge laid against you."

After a two-month war of words, the matter was dropped, apparently without the necessity of sending in Navy gunboats.

It also built for the Admiralty a wide range of facilities including boiler and engineering shops, pump houses and smithies, as well as a submarine torpedo depot. Over the war years, for the Admiralty, alone, the company carried out contracts worth almost £500,000. Like many other key engineering works of the time, in November, 1915, the Minister of Munitions declared Motherwell Bridge to be a "controlled establishment," which meant, essentially, that its complete output, at any time, had to be devoted to the war effort.

The Admiralty's powers were very considerable. They even extended to salaries. When Motherwell Bridge directors wished to increase the salary of the managing director, Alexander C. King when renewing his contract, they had to seek permission to do so.

It was an exceptionally busy period for Motherwell Bridge. Although workers in essential industries were exempt from call-up (conscription was introduced in 1916), many elected to go to the Front anyway - encouraged by local employers who promised that while they were fighting for their country their service pay, lower than civilian wages, would be topped up so that their families and dependants

did not suffer hardship (a promise, it has to be said, which was not always honoured).

There are no records of how many Motherwell Bridge employees enlisted, but the number must have been reasonably substantial, because women were brought in to keep the wheels of industry turning as part of a Government policy to free as many men as possible from factories and works for active service. In 1917, the managing director, Alexander C. King, reported to the directors that fully 50 females were now employed in the work on various machines and acetylene welding and giving "fairly satisfactory results". However, the age's spirit of male chauvinism could hardly have been said to have been breached to any marked extent. The drive to bring women into the work place was known as the Dilution of Labour scheme.

Whatever the directors may have thought privately about employing women in what was regarded as an exclusively male preserve, and having to go to the expense of building ladies' toilets, it certainly didn't do the company any harm. In 1918 it returned a record dividend of 20 per cent to its shareholders.

Annual sales figures for Motherwell Bridge, in 1913, were running at £128,000. By 1918 they had topped £200,000 for the first time, before going on to make another quantum leap to more than £300,000 in 1919.

However, that excellent performance didn't stop the company's local bank manager from carping. Throughout the war, he was in constant correspondence with Motherwell Bridge over the size of its company overdraft, and passing on head office's concerns that the business was still under-capitalised. It was one of the reasons why eventually the directors in 1918 authorised a new issue of 20,000 shares.

Not that the Motherwell Board could be said to be imprudent gentlemen. Incredible as it may sound, in 1916 the managing director, Mr King, reported that he had taken out an insurance policy against the company works and property being damaged by overhead aircraft.

For a town of its size Motherwell's contribution to the war effort, particularly in the manufacture of munitions, was recognised as being second to none in the British Isles. In a somewhat overblown civic account, a review entitled Motherwell's Part in the Great War, a commentator noted: "In the manufacture of munitions of war Motherwell was early 'discovered' by the Ministry of Munitions and Admiralty Departments. Every arm of the Service had some part

of its wants attended to by the workers of Motherwell. Night and day belching smoke and unremitting clangour testified to the workers' earnestness in prosecuting their part in the war. The captains of industry organised their forces on a scale that obtained the highest possible output at a time when the production of munitions was a matter of life and death to the nation. Right nobly did each one play the allotted part, and none more so than the army of women workers ...".

Allowing for the hyperbole of the times, there was solid ground for making such claims. In 1914, King George made a Royal visit to Motherwell, visiting local steelworks and conferring honours on some of its management.

As food rationing began to bite, the Town Council instituted a scheme to create allotments in its public parks. In total, some 54 acres of ground were put under the plough, for growing oats and potatoes.

# Train of Thought...

T.R. MILLER was such a regular traveller by train to London that when he ceased to use the Royal Scot express for the capital, the railway company wrote to him offering to stop the express specially at Symington, Lanarkshire, to pick him up.

A note from the London, Midland and Scottish Railway Company, sent to his home in Biggar, in the 1920s, from the local stationmaster stated: "I haven't noticed you going South for a long time. I had an interview with our General Superintendent the other day and he has granted me permission to allow passengers from Symington to join the Edinburgh portion of the Royal Scot, provided no inconvenience will be caused to passengers from Edinburgh. If the Royal Scot will suit you any time, don't hesitate to let me know."

# Biting off more than you can chew

SOME things never change. Foreigners have always had difficulty in coming to terms with Scotland's national dish, the haggis, as this 1928 letter from Frederick Tench, of the Terry & Tench Company, New York, shows. Writing to T.R. Miller to inquire about participating in the building of a Forth road bridge, he says:

"I was very much delighted a few days ago at receiving a wonderful package of Holy Haggis. Having attended the St. Andrews dinner in New York as well as other functions where the Holy Haggis was served, I was one of the few who knew what Holy Haggis was. However, they all know what it is now ... It certainly was very good of you to think of me in sending me such a nice remembrance."

He wasn't entirely off beam. At some Burns suppers, Americans have been known to have a "holy child" piped in, holding the haggis. They have even gone so far as to have the youngster carried in on a salver.

As the Bard says, "Oh wad some power the giftie gie us, tae see oorsels as ithers see us..."

As for the Forth road bridge construction, a great deal of water had to flow past before the authorities ever got round to doing something about it.

# God's Little Acre–all 66 of them

EVERYTHING T.R. Miller did, he did with style. Until 1930 he lived in Biggar Park House, a large country mansion set in 66 acres of one of the lushest and most scenic areas in Lanarkshire. In 1929, he was paying a total of £64 7s 9d (£64.39p) in rates and other ground burdens for the privilege - including a contribution of £8 11s 4d (£8.57p) towards the stipend of the local Church of Scotland minister.

In 1929 he auctioned off the house. The schedule for the property was quite breathtaking. On the ground floor the entrance porch led into a tiled floor entrance hall with 18th century ceiling. The drawing-room off it, facing south and west, had semi-circular bay windows overlooking parkland to the distant hills. It had an oak parquet floor, an Adams ceiling, fireplace and fender, a panelled dado and was panelled in mauve tapestry.

The smoking room on the opposite side of the hall, some 26 feet by 16 feet, again had a semi-circular bay and oak parquet floor. It was still papered in its original wallpaper with a frieze depicting hunting scenes.

The dining room contained another Adams fireplace and attractive cornice, a panelled dado and glass-doored bookshelves. Off the entrance hall there was also a side door to the garden, via a large cloakroom with its own washbasin and separate W.C.

The schedule continues: "A service pantry with sink and store-room are convenient to the dining room. The domestic accommodation upon the ground floor includes: maids' sitting room; maids' bathroom; kitchen, scullery, larder, store cupboard, laundry and wash-house with three stoneware tubs." There was also a wine cellar.

On the first floor (approached by two staircases) were five principal bed and dressing rooms, and two bathrooms. In the wing were two bedrooms, one sitting room, two servants' bedrooms and housemaids' pantry.

The house had central heating throughout, and its electrical power came from its own generator within the boiler house. At "a short distance from the house" were numerous outbuildings including two garages with the chauffeur's house above them; a secondary garage for two cars, a stable and harness room with hay loft over it, a byre for six cows, a workshop with a store above it, henhouses, a large hay shed and four dog kennels.

While living there, T.R. was very much the local squire. He was Honorary President of the Biggar Burns Club, rode with the local hunt, and was a keen breeder of alsatians, being a member of the Alsatian League and Club of Great Britain. He introduced alsatian breeding to Scotland and was much sought after as a judge.

He was also a member of the Masonic Order, having been admitted to Lodge "The Prince's" No. 607 in West George Street, Glasgow.

His social activities did not end there. He owned a diesel-engine racing yacht, the Caribou, with a captain and one member of crew to sail it in the yacht's own livery, and was a member of both the Clyde Yacht Club and the Clyde Corinthian Yacht Club. In sailing circles his yacht Caribou was nicknamed 'the Carry Booze' because of its well stocked bar. Considering the amount of time he spent travelling to London and abroad, he must have had some difficulties in fulfilling his social commitments.

Only in one respect, did the citizens' patriotism falter. As a war measure, the Burgh Licensing Court prohibited the sale of spirits in public houses, a draconian edict which went through by the narrowest of margins, the casting vote of its chairman. Predictably the whisky ban caused a public outcry - not least from the publicans who raised an action in the Court of Session to get the restriction rescinded.

Their Lordships directed the Burgh Licensing Court to reconsider, and at a special sitting in November, 1916, the ban was repealed. But for six drouthy months, Motherwell had to endure the enforcement of partial prohibition.

Within Motherwell Bridge itself, there were other far reaching decisions as the war wore to a close. In June, 1918, Robert Park, chairman and a founder member of the company, died. T.R. Miller was briefly appointed chairman in his place, to be succeeded in 1921 by John Alston, the son of John M. Alston. In August, 1920, another of Motherwell Bridge's original League of Gentlemen, Alexander C. King, the energetic and active managing director, died. Again, he was to be succeeded by T.R. Miller, on a salary of £1,700 per year.

It was a new decade, the Roaring Twenties. Abroad it was an exuberant, 'feel good'

decade when a war weary world watched wonderingly at the spectacle of America letting down its hair and dancing the Charleston. The hub of it all was the wind-swept city of Chicago, which in addition to spawning the enduring legends of the American hoodlum and the Al Capone era, later to be captured on celluloid, was bursting out in all industrial directions. For Motherwell Bridge, there was to be a Chicago connection - one which was to prove instrumental in the company moving into the big league as a world-wide enterprise.

The man who made it all happen was T.R. Miller. But before that point arrived he had to steer the company through the uncharted waters of a major depression and a period of great social unrest as a British working class sought to force the Government to make good its pledge to create "a home fit for heroes." There was strong pressure for a new social order, while the old one watched, with increasing nervousness, the events unfolding in Russia, where a workers' communist state was being forged. The Great War, and its aftermath, proved to be a crucible where many of the accepted practices of capitalism were put on trial. As in any war, even one of ideas, there were victims on both sides. Many firms went to the wall. T.R. Miller's job was to ensure Motherwell Bridge did not become one of those casualties.

# No Change out of Expenses

IT is heartening to note that accountants were as eagle-eyed over office expense claims 80 years ago as they are today. Being reimbursed for outlays without receipts was a tough job as this 1918 letter to an employee based in Hull shows.

The company bean counter wrote: "In your expenses sheet for last week, the following

items, which I paid without question, appeared, viz:-
*2 lunches - 5s* (25p);
*sundries - 3/4* (17p).
In this week's expenses sheet there appears:
*2 lunches - 5s* (25p);
*sundries - 7/1* (36p) -
which I will pay pending receipt of details from you. My reason for asking for these details to be

supplied in future is so that we may know here who the lunches were for and how the sundries are made up."

The office also took the employee to task for increasing in the time book one of the workmen's rates by a half pence per hour without authorisation, which had to come direct from the managing director.

# It Ain't Half Long, Mum

IN India business was always conducted in English, it being considered "bad form" by the Indians, themselves, to revert to local dialects. Flowery language reached almost an art form at the height of the British Raj.

This piece of correspondence surviving from 1928 from a Mr Dass, a contractor in Madras, is a fairly typical example. It must also have been, as the reader will discover, a strong contender for the "Nae Luck" Award of the Year. His letter states:

"Sirs - With due respect I beg to bring the following few lines before your goodness for kind consideration and favourable orders. Please understand that I have honestly served your Company for about three years in Ceylon, and during the course of my services I lost one of my eyes, on account of sudden fall from the tank. I have come to understand that your honour has to construct 14 oil tanks at Thirukonamalai, Ceylon, at present, and there are about 12 more to be constructed.

"Therefore I beg to request your honour to kindly introduce me to the contractor to allow me piece contract under them so that I may be able to earn a living under your honour's kind patronage.

"Further, I beg to state that I have the honour to declare my right for services under your honour's support for I have lost one of the valuable part of my body (eye) while in your goodness's service ... Under these circumstances stated above, I humbly hope that your honour would kindly do the favour of writing me an introductory letter to the company - for which act of kindness I shall ever pray for you."

Unfortunately for Mr Dass, he was some 66 years premature in his application. Motherwell Bridge had no involvement with the contract. It was carried out by English engineering firm Clayton, Son & Co. which wasn't acquired by Motherwell Bridge until 1994.

# Death on the Roof

THE dangers of erecting oil storage tanks were highlighted at a coroner's inquest into the deaths of three Motherwell Bridge workers, two of whom were blasted off the roof of a 30 feet high tank owned by the Medway Oil Company, at the Isle of Grain in 1925. Another worker was injured. Witnesses told the inquiry that as a riveter started to place a blood-hot rivet in a hole a few feet below the rim of the tank there was a flash of flame from the hole, a dull rumbling and then the top of the tank blew up, hurtling two of the men 10 to 15 feet in the air.

The Coroner's Court also heard that men could only work inside the tank for short periods of time because of intermittent gas vapours, possibly from a faulty valve in a pump which was being used to transmit both water and fuel. The jury found that the explosion had been caused by petrol vapour or other inflammable matter being ignited by a hot rivet. It also found that greater precautions might have been taken by Motherwell Bridge and Medway in view of the workers' discovery of gaseous fumes while working on the tank.

As a future safety precaution it recommended that the practice of using test pipelines for dual functions be discontinued, and that all future cleaning of pipes should be done by steam, failing which no hot rivets should be used after a tank had been connected with the pipeline.

# A Pioneer at the Helm

It is one of life's more universal truths that the sons of famous fathers seldom give as good an account of themselves; it is as if the vigour of the genes have all been used up in a single pioneering generation. However, there are exceptions to the rule - and Thomas R. Miller most certainly was one of them. No history of Motherwell Bridge would be complete without recording the impact he had upon the company's development.

Part showman, part businessman and all autocrat, for most of his 50 years with the company he was the driving force behind its expansion. To the workforce he was something of a God-like figure, with an awesome knowledge of his industry. No aspect of the works' operations was too small for him to inquire into, should it engage his attention; his appetite for information and his attention to detail were insatiable in anything he undertook. He checked everything. And woe betide the unfortunate employee who, in response to his inquiries, tried to cover up lack of knowledge with an imprecise answer, or attempted to defend shoddy workmanship. T.R., a man who commanded instant deference and respect, did not suffer fools - or inferior work - gladly.

Running Motherwell Bridge was more than just his professional occupation. It was both his hobby and his passion; he referred to it grandly, and probably completely unconsciously, as "my company." If the standards of a particular job reflected badly on Motherwell Bridge's image, it was regarded by him as a personal affront - as was anything which affected the good name of the company. That said, he was considered by most to be a fair man. He placed a high premium on plain speaking

and honest answers, but there was no getting away from it: an inquisition by T.R. was an unnerving experience.

He had a mind that was razor-sharp and his analytical powers were considerable. He was not above, either, organising practical experiments to back up his reasoning and deductions. Indeed, right into his seventies, the vigour of his intellectual capacities remained undiminished. He was quite capable of conducting a major inquiry into a contract which had gone awry because of inefficient man and plant management, then producing from his own longhand notes a 50-page report which, for clarity and precision in its reasoning, would have done credit to a High Court judge.

An awesome figure, indeed. With his military background (he served, and was wounded, in the South African War at the turn of the century), he understood full well the mechanics of power and operated the levers of control with skill and considerable panache. He was a good judge of character and adept at picking company personnel. Again, like a good officer, he knew a considerable portion of the works staff by name (this in a works numbering some 500 people) and was acquainted with many of their personal circumstances. Not a lot happened in Motherwell Bridge that didn't reach the ears of T.R. Miller. Throughout his long tenure, his was a familiar figure striding through the works in a well-worn gabardine overcoat (which few people realised was beautifully fur-lined), checking everything was as it should be. T.R. insisted on high standards of neatness and tidiness.

**T.R. MILLER.**
Thomas Ronald Miller, with fifty years at director level in the company, was the longest serving director.

Not a cigarette end or a match stick was allowed to blemish the works grounds.

Indeed, the work force developed its own early warning system to alert others that T.R. was doing his rounds. Whenever they spotted him, they started beating metal on metal, much in the way that Irish housewives in Nationalist sectors of Northern Ireland would clang dustbin lids to alert neighbours that a military patrol was in the street. The analogy is not misplaced: T.R. Miller was on patrol. Most days, when at Motherwell Bridge, he would make a regular tour at 4 pm, supplementing that round of the works with other visits.

WORKS STAFF. Works staff circa 1928. Front (l to r): seated John Jarvie, foreman driller, James Walker, foreman blacksmith and George Crichton, foreman engineer. Back: John Anderson, foreman template loft, James Cowan, works manager, John Moffat, foreman marking shop and William Anderson, foreman fitting shop.

SITE VISIT.
An early photograph of T.R. Miller (second from right) with M. McKay, D. Young and R. Craig.

BENDING ROLLS. A photograph taken in the early 1920s showing a plate bending rolls operator checking the curvature of the plate utilising a wooden template. This machine would have been installed for the rolling of plates for oil storage tanks, an early diversification from bridges, which proved to be a valuable product for many years. Storage tank work was particularly important in the depression years between the wars.

From the access gallery which ran the full length of the 700-foot main workshop, he was monarch of all he surveyed. Therein, perhaps, lay the eternal fascination of Motherwell Bridge for T.R. Miller; there is something awe-inspiring about heavy engineering, watching ant-like figures manoeuvring and fashioning great metal structures. One suspects he never completely lost his sense of wonder at watching them being created.

To sum up, as a leading industrialist of his day, the twice-married T.R. had many of the virtues, and some of the vices, of such men; he worked, and played, hard and had a very considerable ego. He projected an aura of importance in everything he did. If that is a less than flattering pen picture, it should be added that large industrial concerns are not run by shrinking violets.

In the 1920s, in assuming the mantle of managing director, T.R. Miller truly came into his own. The man who a decade earlier used to be criticised by his brothers for arriving at the office, on occasion, in his fox-hunting pinks - a dilettante approach which they frowned upon - now occupied the key position in the company. Through it he was to stamp his personality on the business.

He was 42 years of age when he assumed full control, a time in most industrialists' lives when they have left the mistakes of their youth behind them, and where their management style tends to be a blend of experience as well as dynamism. T.R. Miller's arrival at the helm was to signal a new drive forward. His appointment as managing director coincided with a radical internal re-organisation of the works management structure following the death of previous managing director Alexander King; the company had grown to such a size that it was no longer possible for it to continue efficiently without laying down well defined areas of responsibility.

MAIN PICTURE: PONTOON ROOF FOR IRAQ. Trial assembly at the works of a Wiggins pontoon floating roof for a 120 feet diameter storage tank for Iraq Petroleum Co. Limited.

INSET TOP: TANK SHELL UNDER CONSTRUCTION. Erection of the fourth tier on a riveted tank at the Bowling Terminal on the Firth of Clyde.

INSET BOTTOM: TANK BASE UNDER CONSTRUCTION. Erection of the bottom of a storage tank on temporary supports to assist the riveting of the plates before being lowered into its final position.

SET: TANK ROOF. Trial assembly of a Wiggins pan-type floating roof for an 82 feet 6 inches diameter storage tank. Motherwell Colliery can be seen in the background.

Mr David Young, as the £550 a year technical manager, was made responsible for contracts estimating, the works drawing office and supervision of all shop work, reporting directly to the Board on technical matters. Mr Peter Bruce was appointed outside manager, handling outside erection work, and reporting directly to Mr Young; Mr Andrew Cowan, the works manager, was responsible for workers' efficiency and plant maintenance - again under the supervision of Mr Young. Under the new set-up, workmen's rates were to be settled mutually between Mr Orr and Mr Young, in consultation with the parties in charge of the job.

Within a year, these important changes, instituted in August 1920, were to be rocked by an obviously traumatic episode. In January, 1921, Motherwell Bridge's company secretary John Orr was dismissed, with T.R. Miller being appointed secretary and commercial manager as a temporary measure.

DAVID YOUNG.
David Clews Young, general manager, and later a director of the company from 1935 till his death in January 1959.

Ten months later, in November, 1921, John Orr was reinstated as company secretary, only to find himself again in hot water two years later over his drinking. This time he was demoted, being offered a subordinate position in the company's counting house at a salary of £250, a loss in wages of £100 a year. Motherwell Bridge cost accountant Joseph M. Anderson was appointed company secretary and Orr ceased to play an important role in the organisation. Meanwhile, Motherwell Bridge had business challenges of a more normal nature on its agenda during that period. Chief among them was the electrification of the works.

For many years the company had staved off a decision on whether or not to take its power from outside sources - at that time a plethora of small private and municipal companies. Unable to gain sufficient guarantees that the level of power it needed would be forthcoming, it had continued to generate its own electricity for all its functions.

MAIN PICTURE: WIGGINS ROOF. A Wiggins Roof for a 117 feet storage tank under trial assembly in the works yard prior to delivery to the Anglo-Persian Oil Co. Limited during 1927.
The floating roof had been devised to stop evaporation on storage tanks, and was designed to ride directly on the surface of the product, over which it formed an effective blanket preventing air from having access to the product and carrying it off in the form of evaporation. The Wiggins roof was the first successful type to be introduced to the market and was of 'pan' type conception. Floating roof design was developed later by Chicago Bridge engineers culminating in the modern Type 5 single deck roof and the double deck roof. The roof itself was slightly less than the tank shell in diameter to allow for vertical movement. Contact with the shell was through thin plates held in position by springs attached to the roof and the gap between these thin plates and the roof itself covered with a flexible rubber (later neoprene) membrane.
The photograph shows the view to the west and the undeveloped nature of the north Motherwell area at that time.

INSET: PLATING DEPARTMENT. A photograph of the platers taken during September 1929. The platers' job was to assemble the plate sections and structural members which in their day often required full trial erection in the works yard.
Seated front left William Carruthers, and William Wilson rear row right.

ut in 1921 it decided to hook-up to an outside supplier. That electrification (to Clyde Valley Power Company) was achieved in the summer of 1922, after the end of the Fair holidays. It cost the company in excess of £14,000 to ready the plant for the change-over and install its new electrical transformer house. There were other major improvements, too. That same year the foundations for an expansion to the office buildings were laid and by April of the following year the £17,000 extension was complete. In 1923, an entirely new bay within the main shop was also constructed.

There was one other change instituted in the following year, in September, 1924, which stood well above the warp and woof of normal commercial development: by special resolution of the shareholders, the company changed its name to the Motherwell Bridge & Engineering Company Limited. The company minutes of

BELOW: BRIDGE TRIAL ERECTION. Trial erection of the Grey Street span bridge for South African Railways, taking place during 1930 at the rear of the Bridge Works. In the foreground are replacement trough deck sections for other bridges for South African Railways.
The pressing of trough sections from plate was an early development by the company, which gave it a market through to the late 1960s.

the time noted: "It was found the present name was too restrictive and was prejudicing the company, particularly with the opening up of connections abroad."

The change of name was a clear move by the company away from its "blacksmithing" roots (as rivals disparagingly described them) to build upon its rapidly growing reputation as engineers. For clients abroad there was a 'comfort factor' in dealing with a structural engineering company: the UK was recognised as a centre of excellence in that field.

The early development of overseas contracts by the company, which had been undertaken sporadically in the previous decade, are not overly well chronicled. Peppered through the company's early accounts are occasional references to contracts for abroad, but the preponderance of work remained within the United Kingdom.

What can be said with confidence, however, is that by the mid-1920s Motherwell Bridge's foreign enterprises were surprisingly well established, it having opened up countries like China and South Africa.

LEFT: WORKS EXTENSION. During 1925 the company extended the works by the addition of a modern full length bay.

# A Fishy Explanation

THE holy of holies at Motherwell Bridge was T.R. Miller's office. No-one dared set foot inside it without permission, so it was only when T.R. was on holiday that maintenance checks could be carried out. Seizing his chance while T.R. was away, Jock Anderson, then assistant works manager, rounded up a squad to check the electrical fixtures. The company "spark" of the day was Jimmy Currie, and Jock was very punctilious in his instructions not to disturb anything and to cover up the desk well before removing a glass bowl from the light fitting to replace a bulb.

Jimmy started to unscrew the fitting when without warning it came crashing down and smashed to smithereens. There had been a small ceiling leak and the water had all but filled the bowl, making it too heavy for the loosened screws. An exact replica being unavailable, a different fitting was mounted and the room restored to pristine condition.

However, on T.R.'s return, Jock was summoned to explain why the light bowl had been changed. The explanation was accepted.

A few days later T.R. sent for Jock again, this time to investigate a strong odour coming from its fine leather armchairs. The source was quickly found. Unbeknown to anyone, the cleaners had been using T.R.'s inner sanctum as an unofficial canteen, and someone had left a half-eaten fish supper down the side of a chair!

# CHAPTER 5

In 1927, under the supervision of T.R. Miller, the company produced a most wonderful brochure on Motherwell Bridge's span of activities. Containing information in three languages - English, French and Spanish - and lavishly illustrated, the brochure was years ahead of its time and is a quite superb example of the printer's art, which for clarity, presentation and design could not be bettered today. It gives a picture of a surprisingly extensive network of foreign interests.

**THE BROWN BOOK.** The 'Brown Book' as it is affectionately known was produced during 1927 under the supervision of T.R.Miller and lavishly illustrates the span of activities of the company in three languages – English, French and Spanish.

By 1927 the company had agents representing it in offices in Johannesburg, South Africa; Cairo, Egypt; Christchurch, New Zealand and in Bangkok in what was then known as Siam. By now describing itself as both engineers and contractors, Motherwell Bridge stated it was capable of undertaking structural steel and ironwork of every description, including: bridges, roofs, steel-frame buildings, crane girders and gantries, pithead frames, towers, chimneys, riveted kilns and tubes, piers, jetties, pontoons, dock gates, caissons, oil storage tanks, water tanks, pressed steel troughing, railway sleepers and guttering.

The company, at that juncture, was capable of turning out annually some 36,000 tons of finished structural and pressed steel work from what was one of the most extensive and modern works anywhere in Britain.

It was also capable of undertaking the largest of contracts, with success, for "the British Isles, the larger British Dominions and Colonies". At times it had as many as 4,000 men engaged in outside erection work.

A flick through the brochure's 80 beautiful, photogravured pages (now a collectors' item, since only 2,000 of the catalogues were produced) is to meet at every turn the romance of an industrial age which pioneered the world's transport systems. Motherwell Bridge's accomplishments were impressive: a famous 300-foot girder bridge for the Shanghai, Hangchow, Ningpo Railway; an immense 38-span viaduct bridge across the swirling waters of the Zwie-Zwie River in Nyasaland, now Malawi, at the Zambesi River for the Central South African Company; road bridges near Bombay for the Great Indian Peninsula Railway; bridges for the South African Railways and the Basutoland Government; a massive extension to the Victoria Station in Bombay; locomotive erecting shops at Parel, India; oil and water storage tanks for countries ranging from Persia, Australia and Aden to Singapore; dock gates for Bombay harbour; the construction, export and erection of a 180-ton giant hammerhead crane in Nagasaki, Japan.

Let us not forget, either, that this was an era when air travel was in its infancy, as were telecommunications. There were no tailor-made dock extensions for unloading equipment. Many of the sites lay in remote countryside. When a Motherwell Bridge squad departed on a foreign contract it had to be self-sufficient in every single department of the operation. Every bolt, every rivet, every last component, had to be loaded on board ship. There was no question of ordering in spares. A missed consignment of material could mean a six months delay in delivery as the cargo ship plied its way slowly round a circuit of ports.

Frequently the supervisor would have to improvise on unloading arrangements because in third world countries the facilities were inadequate or non-existent. There were language and cultural barriers to be dealt with, not to mention the extremes of foreign climates. Undertaking a Motherwell Bridge contract abroad called for initiative, resourcefulness and a genuinely pioneering spirit. Yet still these magnificent edifices were constructed to a standard of excellence which was a credit to the company.

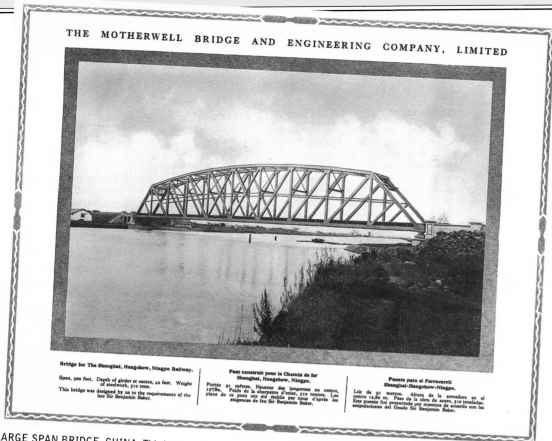

THE MOTHERWELL BRIDGE AND ENGINEERING COMPANY, LIMITED

| Bridge for The Shanghai, Hangchow, Ningpo Railway. | Pont construit pour le Chemin de fer Shanghai, Hangchow, Ningpo. | Puente para el Ferrocarril Shanghai-Hangchow-Ningpo. |
|---|---|---|
| Span, 300 feet. Depth of girder at centre, 42 feet. Weight of steelwork, 510 tons. This bridge was designed by us to the requirements of the late Sir Benjamin Baker. | Portée 91 mètres. Hauteur des longerons au centre, 12m80. Poids de la charpente d'acier, 510 tonnes. Les plans de ce pont ont été établis par nous d'après les exigences de feu Sir Benjamin Baker. | Luz de 91 metros. Altura de la armadura en el centro 12,80 m. Peso de la obra de acero, 510 toneladas. Este puente fué proyectado por nosotros de acuerdo con las estipulaciones del finado Sir Benjamin Baker. |

LARGE SPAN BRIDGE, CHINA. This bridge with some 300 feet span was designed and erected for the Shanghai, Hangchow, Ningpo Railway in 1915/16. The depth of the girders at the centre was 42 feet and there were 510 tons of steelwork used.

THE MOTHERWELL BRIDGE AND ENGINEERING COMPANY, LIMITED

| Locomotive Erecting Shops at Parel, India, for the Great Indian Peninsula Railway (View of Travesty Bay). | Ateliers de montage de locomotives, construits à Parel, aux Indes, pour le Chemin de fer Great Indian Peninsula (Vue de la travée " Travesty "). | Talleres de montaje de locomotoras en Parel, India, para el Great Indian Peninsula Railway. Vista de la nave Travesty. |
|---|---|---|
| These shops consist of four bays, each 56 feet wide and two bays each 65 feet wide and 720 feet long. The contract included all steelwork in columns, roofing, roof girders, gantry girders, etc. Weight of steelwork, 4,630 tons. Engineers : Messrs. Robert White & Partners. | Ces ateliers consistent en quatre travée de 17 mètres de largeur et deux de 20 mètres, toutes d'une longueur de 219 mètres, et l'entreprise comprenait tous les ouvrages d'acier en fait de colonnes, combles, sommiers, longerons de portiques, etc., d'un poids total de 4.630 tonnes. Ingénieurs : MM. Robert White and Partners. | Estos talleres se componen de 4 naves de 17 metros y 2 naves de 20 metros cada una de las cuales mide 219 metros de longitud. La contrata comprendía todas las obras de acero relativas á columnas, armaduras de techos, vigas para techos, vigas para pórticos, &c., con un peso total de 4.630 toneladas de acero. Ingenieros : Sres. Robert White and Partners. |

RAILWAY WORKSHOPS, INDIA. These locomotive erecting shops at Parel, India were built for the Great Indian Peninsula Railway. The shops consist of four bays, each 56 feet wide and two bays each 65 feet wide and some 720 feet long. The contract included all the steelwork in columns, roofing, roof girders, gantry girders, etc. Weight of steelwork involved was over 4,630 tons. The view shown in the photograph is of the section of the workshops known as the 'Travesty' Bay.

Motherwell Bridge's involvement in the infrastructure of the United Kingdom was no less impressive: 17 railway bridges near Aberdeen; a 600 feet bridge, 180 feet above the River Tees; a bridge over the River Clyde at Uddingston, with three spans of 90 feet; a bridge across the Tay with five spans of 100 feet; 36 bridges in Paisley and Barrhead; another ten at Muirkirk; a swing railway bridge across the Forth and Clyde Canal; 37 bridges for the Dalry and North Johnstone Railway; and, closer to home, in the year of 1926, a bridge across the River Clyde carrying the main road between Motherwell and Hamilton. The list goes on and on, well beyond the random selection presented here.

Equally, the diversity of work being undertaken by Motherwell Bridge in those early decades was considerable. One of the more unusual jobs was the erection of two 136 feet high cooling towers for the Corporation of Edinburgh's electricity department. The London architect who designed them wanted the iron towers to resemble masonry, so Motherwell Bridge faced them in cast-iron - and highly decorative, as well as functional, they were, too.

It was not, however, joy unalloyed.

The post-war years heralded a worldwide slump in the demand for steel, triggered by a collapse in shipbuilding on the Clyde after shipowners bought up cheaply a defeated Germany's merchant navy. British industry and

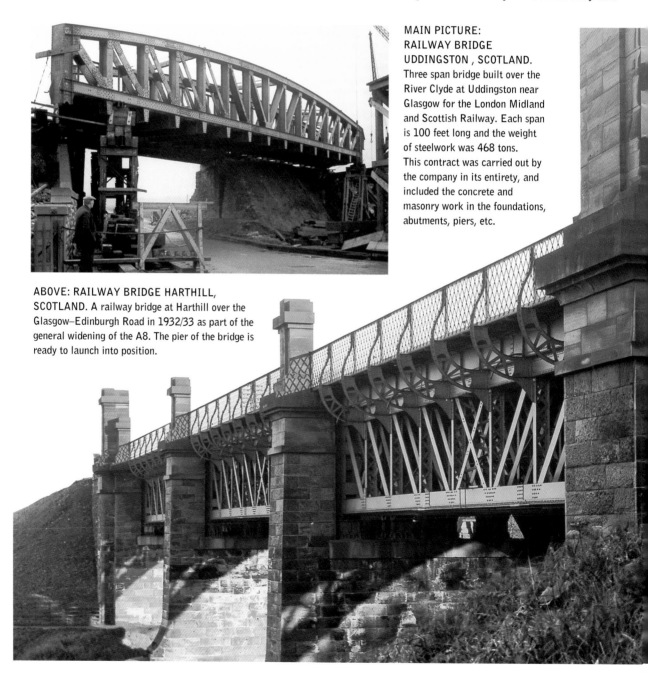

MAIN PICTURE:
RAILWAY BRIDGE
UDDINGSTON , SCOTLAND.
Three span bridge built over the River Clyde at Uddingston near Glasgow for the London Midland and Scottish Railway. Each span is 100 feet long and the weight of steelwork was 468 tons. This contract was carried out by the company in its entirety, and included the concrete and masonry work in the foundations, abutments, piers, etc.

ABOVE: RAILWAY BRIDGE HARTHILL, SCOTLAND. A railway bridge at Harthill over the Glasgow–Edinburgh Road in 1932/33 as part of the general widening of the A8. The pier of the bridge is ready to launch into position.

commerce failed to recover many of its pre-war markets abroad. In 1921, faced with a 20 per cent cut in wages, Scotland's miners went on strike. The knock-on effect of that three-month bitter struggle saw Motherwell and Wishaw overwhelmed by unemployment which first doubled, then trebled to more than 12,000 by 1923 as, one by one, firms were forced to close down.

Almost alone among the steel finishing trades in those bleak years, Motherwell Bridge pressed forward with its major works improvements, while being highly selective about what contracts it took on. Indeed, as prices collapsed, it refrained from tendering for many jobs and judiciously lowered prices to retain important customers. One of those was the Anglo-Persian Oil

Company, for whom it was building 10 storage tanks.

With an eye to the future, the directors took the unusual step of reducing the cost of the job to the client after it had commenced. In another ingenious solution to the financial climate, the directors toyed with building five giant storage tanks on the Isle of Grain, and taking payment from the £5,000 a year rent they would generate for the oil company. In the event, they more prudently negotiated a deal of payment for the work over a period of two years. But it shows the sort of financial stratagems the company had to resort to; more than ever before, trading was a mixture of caution and specially constructed financial arrangements.

Beyond the works gates, the political turmoil continued. The removal of rent controls in 1920 saw some landlords push up rents by 40 per cent, triggering off rent strikes and evictions. In Motherwell the populace

BELOW: COOLING TOWERS. The company carried out the entire erection work, both steel and cast iron of these cooling towers for the Corporation of Edinburgh in 1911/12. The towers are 137 feet high and measure 40 feet wide at the base. They required 570 tons of steelwork and their steel framing was faced with cast iron work to represent masonry.

physically reinstated families in their homes, defying factors, sheriff's officers and police. It was a time of open discontent and sullen resentment as impoverished families sought to cope with the collapse of the local economy, mass unemployment and poor housing conditions. Parish relief and poverty held sway.

As the clashes between the forces of capitalism and socialism intensified, left-wing militants within the I.L.P. (Independent Labour Party) and the Communist Party swept the municipal elections. The stridency of political agitation was everywhere to be heard, gaining the town the label of 'Red Motherwell.'

Through it all, Motherwell Bridge kept going. The worst year of all was 1926, the year of the General Strike. For eight days Britain was brought to a standstill. Again it was the miners who led the battle in a bitter lock-out that in Scotland was to drag on for seven long months. In Motherwell, the General Strike passed off relatively incident-free, save for several arrests of pickets and an attempt by unknown persons to blow up a railway line at Holytown. In its first edition after the strike ended, the local paper reported that the parish council had met until well past midnight to consider 1,600 applications for temporary relief from people flung out of work.

After the TUC called off the General Strike, the Scottish miners' lock-out continued until November. They were literally starved into submission. In Lanarkshire all that stood between their unfortunate families and the soup kitchen was a meagre Parish relief allowance of 3s 6d to 6s (17p to 30p) a week per adult and half a crown (12$\frac{1}{2}$p) per child. Such was the poverty, Dalziel Parish Council paid out £16,000 to miners' dependants between May and November that year. In a test case raised in the name of David Colville and Sons, major Lanarkshire employers, including Motherwell Bridge, challenged the legality of Dalziel Parish Council disbursing poor relief to miners' families, hoping to bring the miners' dispute to an earlier conclusion. However, the Court of Session did not hand down a ruling in favour of the employers until December, by which time the strike had ended.

MAIN PICTURE: STONEFERRY BRIDGE, HULL. The company supplied and erected this Stoneferry swing bridge for Hull Corporation in 1904 and its length was 145 feet and the width 21 feet. The steelwork involved weighed 332 tons.

ABOVE: ZWIE-ZWIE BRIDGE, NYASALAND. This bridge, over the Zwie-Zwie River, Nyasaland, now Malawi, between Port Herald and the Zambesi River, has 38 spans, giving a total length of 2,000 feet. The weight of the steelwork was 1,850 tons. The erection of the viaduct was carried out under Motherwell Bridge supervision circa 1914.

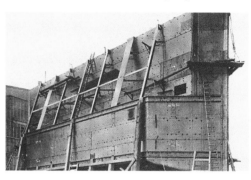

ABOVE: DOCK CAISSON, BOMBAY. This view shows the floating caisson for Victoria Dock, Bombay, being temporarily erected at the Motherwell Works circa 1912. The width of the entrance was 80 feet and the depth of the caisson 42 feet, beam 23 feet and the weight of steelwork 380 tons.

ABOVE: NAGASAKI CRANE. In this print this 180-ton giant hammerhead crane is undergoing erection at Nagasaki, Japan, circa 1908. The length of the cantilever girder was 247 feet, height of the pedestal 135 feet, and the weight of steelwork was 370 tons. Motherwell Bridge personnel supervised the erection of the crane at Nagasaki.

ABOVE: DADAR ROAD BRIDGE, INDIA. This bridge carries the Dadar Road over the railway at Bombay, and consists of five skew spans and ten square spans supported on braced piers. The roadway is 40 feet wide with two 10 feet footpaths. The total length of the bridge is 865 feet and it has 2,386 tons of steelwork. It was produced for the Great Indian Peninsula Railway.

In fairness, it should be said that support of the test case was not entirely an example of flint-hearted capitalism on the part of Motherwell Bridge. Normally the company exhibited a reasonable degree of social concern towards its workforce and the larger community; indeed within months of the strike being broken it was donating cash towards the Miners' Distress Fund. However, in 1926 a large portion of big business was fighting for its very existence. In life, there are no apologies for survival.

From May until September of that dreadful year, Motherwell Bridge was able to continue operations because it was dependent upon electricity, rather than coal, to power its machinery. However, when its steel supply became exhausted all work was forced to cease, considerably denting company profits. Everywhere, industry was battening down the hatches in expectations of still tougher times ahead. Yet in a review of its order book, Motherwell Bridge was able to report that it had a year's work in hand - very considerably above the norm. For that healthy state of affairs, T.R. Miller and his directors deserve considerable credit; they had successfully negotiated the treacherous rapids of social and economic change, keeping the company in healthy financial shape.

From the mid-twenties, Motherwell Bridge emerged fitter and better equipped for trade than just about any of its competitors - a fact that did not pass unnoticed elsewhere in the world. On April 11, 1927, a letter arrived at the company headquarters from the USA's largest fabricators of tanks, the Chicago Bridge & Iron Works, offering it the opportunity to manufacture and erect, under licence, a revolutionary new type of oil storage tank roof which dramatically reduced the amount of fuel evaporation, and the potential danger of fire hazards. It was known as the Wiggins roof.

At the time, conventional storage tanks had fixed roofs, which meant that every time a tank was emptied a gap between the surface of the oil and the roof occurred. Nature abhorring a vacuum, the space was quickly filled with volatile and highly inflammable gases "boiling" off the surface, which had to be vented when the tank was again topped up. In the case of lighter petroleum oils, the loss of fuel through evaporation, particularly in hot climates, was considerable. It was also dangerous. The risk of gases being ignited as they came in contact with oxygen in the air during venting was an ever-present fire hazard every time the tank was refilled.

# FLASHES OF INSPIRATION

TO be a gaffer at Motherwell Bridge, your first name had to be Jock - or certainly it seemed that way. There were a lot of them about. In the electrical department the gaffer was Jock Brock, who was very much the fount of all knowledge. Whenever there was a problem to be solved, he was the man to keep everybody right.

On one occasion he was summoned to the big bay where a 100-ton vessel had been lifted and conveyed down the shop. Unfortunately, the load couldn't be released because one of the crane's contactors refused to stay in. Jock clambered up onto the crane rail and, with a welder, organised an "airborne" weld which took them virtually along the whole length of the bay. They then descended into the crane cabin to get to grips with the faulty contactor.

In the cab, Jock delivered a homily to his companion on the dangers of having to deal with such matters and having to walk along crane rails. Having completed the lecture, he used a pencil to ram home the faulty contactor, whereupon a great flash of electricity surged down it - causing Jock, generally a man of few words, to say a little more than usual.

Another gaffer in the template loft was Johnny Paterson, a one-time hard man fast with his fists and able to hold his own with any man, until he saw the light and became a Christian. Asked by T.R. to make a 'keep off the grass' notice, Johnny delegated the job to one of the young lads. Knowing that T.R. was bound to inspect it, the youth made an excellent job of the board before thankfully returning to his own work. Alas, he had performed the task too well. When Johnny saw the result he got him to make another half dozen - for his church.

CHAPTER 5

## DOG DAY AFTERNOON...

DOGS and the Miller family went together like bacon and eggs. Ronald Miller, son of T. R. Miller having a particular fondness for the larger breeds, bought himself an Irish wolfhound which he named Phutt, reputedly after his former army batman in India. It was a beautiful animal but like many of its breed was highly strung and rather timid. Having thoroughly trained it, one day he decided to walk it through the works off the leash.

Unfortunately as he was walking down the shop floor a large metal component was dropped with an almighty crash. Startled by the loud noise, the dog took to its heels, with Ronald Miller in hot pursuit shouting, "Phutt, phutt .. " All across the factory workmen's jaws dropped. They thought they were witnessing the boss running through the works bellowing the 'F' word.

Within months there was a follow-up meeting in the Hague in Holland and before the year was out a deal had been struck - although it took the lawyers, as ever, somewhat longer to catch up with the terms of the handshake.

What was finally settled upon was an agreement involving Chicago Bridge, Motherwell Bridge and one of its principal competitors, the Whessoe Foundry and Engineering Company, of Darlington. Under the agreement, Motherwell Bridge and Whessoe were licensed to manufacture and sell Wiggins floating and breather roofs exclusively throughout the UK and Ireland, all British colonies, protectorates and

SOUTH WALES TANKAGE. A general view of fixed roof storage tanks built by Motherwell Bridge at the Anglo-Persian Oil Company oil storage depot at Skewen, near Neath, South Wales.
By the 1920s Motherwell Bridge had already completed 300 storage tanks for the Anglo-Persian Company with a total of 35,000 tons of steelwork. The Anglo-Persian Oil Company later became the Anglo-Iranian Oil Company and finally British Petroleum.

mandated territories, including the "Empire of India and the Kingdom of Egypt." The companies were also permitted, on a non-exclusive basis, to manufacture and sell to all other countries the Wiggins products until such time as the US company had arranged sub-licences with them.

Chicago Bridge's decision to select two companies within Britain to handle Wiggins roofs came about because each enjoyed the backing of one of the two major oil companies of the day. To keep everyone happy, the US firm decided a tandem approach would better ensure rapid development of the commercial territories ceded to them, thereby maximising its royalties.

And, indeed, the Wiggins inventions sold and erected by Motherwell Bridge proved an instant success with the oil industry. The very first order Motherwell Bridge received was for three Wiggins roofs for the Anglo-Persian Company in October, 1927. By mid 1929 the company had landed several extremely large contracts for the devices. The company was also vigorously expanding its foreign operations, taking on new contracts in India, Burma and Australia. The Chicago Bridge deal, in fact, was a milestone in company development. It generated a great deal of business for the company down the decades. Building floating and breather roof tankage under licence was a long-term revenue-earner. For several years at the beginning of the licensing agreement, it was a mainstay of company profitability. It had come along at precisely the right time, for just round the corner was another, and much deeper, world-wide depression triggered off by the great Wall Street stock market crash of 1929. Without its foreign trade, Motherwell Bridge would not have weathered as well as it did the Hungry Thirties.

# SERVICE WITH A GROWL

A 1928 MARMON. Straight Eight Coupe with wire wheels and dickie seat, a typical example of the Marmon of that era.

ONE of the abiding passions of T.R. Miller's life was a love of expensive, exotic cars. But he demanded of the manufacturers perfection and went to great lengths to obtain satisfaction while the vehicle was still under guarantee. He was also an inveterate letter writer with an extensive knowledge of mechanical matters - for the luckless dealers a fairly devastating combination.

In 1928, exclusive London dealers Pass and Joyce Ltd (telegrams, 'Bestocars, London') were on the receiving end of a typical T.R. blast over his recent purchase of a Marmon car. It all started out amicably enough. Pass and Joyce wrote to T.R. asking if he would let a potential buyer see his model, as they had no facilities to show the Marmon

car in Scotland.

They also unwisely said: "In accordance with our usual custom, we are taking this opportunity of writing to say that if there is any assistance we can render, we trust you will not hesitate to avail yourself of our services."

T.R. did not hesitate. "Sirs - I forward to you under separate cover the two cones of outer roller race from the off front wheel of the Marmon car. The material appears to have been defective from the start and has not been properly case-hardened. A serious defect like this does not inspire confidence as it tends to generate a feeling of mistrust that there may be other defective structural parts ... The Chauffeur observed when washing the car down after my return home that

the off front wheel was dangerously slack. I had him strip the wheel in my presence. On examination the wheel was fully one-quarter of an inch from its correct seat ... I shall be glad to have your full report at your convenience in connection with this matter, and trust that the spare parts were sent by first passenger train, as arranged with you this morning."

Pass and Joyce replied: "We are distressed to note that in view of a ball race (roller bearing) having given out you mistrust the other structural parts of the car, but really and truly, the writer would like to point out that these are manufactured by Timkins and not by the Marmon Company, and although in this instance it is regrettable that one should have given out, we can assure you it is a very uncommon occurrence ... If you would care for us to take this up with the factory we shall be only too happy to do so, but are afraid they could not tell you any further than the remarks contained in this letter."

Within five days, Pass and Joyce were writing again - less cockily. "Dear Mr Miller - I was sorry to hear that the ball race sent you was not suitable for the front wheel on your Marmon car. I sincerely hope that the one despatched to you yesterday by passenger train reached you safely and that you have had same fitted."

There was an interregnum of one month, then the war of words resumed.

T. R. Miller wrote: "I am returning under separate cover for your inspection the set of sparking plugs. You will note seven of the eight are burnt out. The car has done 5,000 miles and it is very disappointing to find that these plugs have not stood up to the test.

"I had a great deal of trouble before I found the actual fault was due to the ignition. I have now replaced these plugs. I assume that you will recompense me for this extra incurred. My own opinion is that the engine generates a heat too great for these plugs to stand up to and I shall be interested to learn your views ... The springs of the front cushion are coming through the canvas underneath and will require to be re-fixed. I shall be glad to learn if I may send this to be repaired by one of our local coach-builders, and debit the

charge to yourselves."

Back came yet another letter from Pass and Joyce: "I am in receipt of your letters of 15th and 17th inst. I have refrained from answering the first before now as I was hoping to hear from the factory, relative to the ball races replaced in the front wheel ... However, the parts were replaced free of charge under the guarantee and I trust to let you have further information as soon as it comes to hand.

"I note you have experienced some little difficulty with the Champion plugs. My Stores are sending you a set of new plugs which the Champion people have designed specially for the Marmon engine. These are for free replacement.

"I am sorry to hear about the springs in the front cushion but really and truly I am afraid Pass and Joyce cannot hold themselves responsible for work carried out apart from their own Service Station. Should you be in Town we shall be only too happy to look into this matter ..."

It is not recorded whether the potential Scottish buyer of a Marmon car ever visited T.R. Perhaps Pass and Joyce wisely refrained from asking.

Almost a decade later T.R., now driving a 25 H.P. Rolls Royce, was still spiritedly conducting his one man crusade against

the motor trade. The Sales Department of Jack Barclay Ltd., of London, wrote to T.R. offering him a spin in a new 3-litre Bentley, with the comment: "I have been wondering how your 25 H.P. Rolls-Royce has been behaving and whether you are still of the opinion that its acceleration is not what you had anticipated ...".

Already winging its way to London was a complaint about the self-starter which T.R. had had to have replaced at a cost of £1 3s 9d (£1.19p) when the car wouldn't start at Dumfries. Naturally, the company agreed to compensate Mr Miller for the repair.

Two months later, for the third time, the starter broke down which necessitated T.R. sending his chauffeur down to London to have the whole starter unit replaced. Free of charge.

## PLAYING A BLINDER

ONE of the great characters of Motherwell Bridge was the outside squad erection foreman, John McKie. He was noted for two things: he had only one eye and he chewed tobacco. He also didn't take kindly to being quizzed about his work. When he was put in charge of building the works pickling plant, a young Chris Fleming-Brown, a grandson of T. R. Miller, was keen to find out how he intended to erect the portal frames.

Twice young Chris asked him but each time the foreman fobbed him off and turned away to attend to his work. The third time the question came, McKie half-turned towards the young inquirer, and discharged a long stream of tobacco juice which went all over the front of Chris's boiler suit.

With a glint of satisfaction in his good eye, he apologised, saying: "Very sorry, son. You were on my blind side."

# Wooden Guns to Stave off Invaders

It was a scene which could have stepped straight from the popular TV comedy series, Dad's Army. In the time office of Motherwell Bridge on a Saturday night a group of company workers sat disconsolately peering out into the gloom, wondering how their mates were enjoying themselves. Not for them the pleasure of a couple of pints with their friends down at the local pub, or a chaff with the girls at a dance or church hall social before curfew. Their duty as Local Defence Volunteers - later called the Home Guard - was an all-night stint guarding the works premises which, as in the First World War, were again an important cog in the United Kingdom's war machine.

Even though there were usually four or five of them on duty, few liked the assignment. Charlie Higgins, now 80, of Calder View, Motherwell, who worked for the company from 1935 to 1981, recalls: "You had to do compulsory night shift, sitting in the time office. It wasn't very popular because it always fell at weekends.

You did your stint, then it would come round again three or four weekends later."

In the time office all that Motherwell Bridge's finest had to stave off any invasion by Hitler's legions were wooden guns similar to those used by the Boys' Brigade, supplemented by two genuine rifles. The ammunition for them, however, was not exactly to hand. It was locked some distance away in the main offices in the safe of company secretary Forbes D. Masterton, a man whose thrift - not to say parsimony - on behalf of the company had already reached legendary proportions. It was rumoured that to get a new pencil from him staff had first to turn in the stub of the old one.

Quite what the security detail was to do in the event of invasion was never entirely clear to those taking their turn on the regular roster of night guard duty which came round every few weekends. Some reckoned it was

HOME GUARD. Officers and NCOs of the Motherwell Bridge Works Home Guard in camp at Biggar in July 1942.
Back (l to r); L/Cp J.B. Fleming, L/Cp A. Crone, L/Cp A.S. Banks, L/Cp G. Templeton, L/Cp P. McGregor, L/Cp J. Stewart.
Middle: Corp R.L. Muir, Sgt E. McDade, Sgt J. MacDonald, CSM R.D. Carrie, Sgt J. Taylor, Corp T.H. Purves, L/Cp W. McCarrison.
Seated: 2/Lt Brown, Lieut Forbes D. Masterton.

probably more feasible to take on the invaders bare-handed than to attempt to part Mr Masterton from any company assets reposing in his office safe. Fortunately, the theory was never required to be put to the test.

For an industrial area of huge importance to the war effort, Motherwell and central Lanarkshire escaped virtually unscathed from air raids. Unlike Clydebank and Greenock, which were subjected to some of the severest incendiary bombing in Britain, only seven bombs were dropped in and around Motherwell and Wishaw throughout the entire duration of the war. Only two came anywhere close to Motherwell Bridge - a 20lb bomb which blasted a crater near the main railway line at Ghillies Lane and Bellshill Road, and a second which again detonated fairly close to the Bellshill Road.

However, the people of Lanarkshire were not to know that they were not a primary target for the Luftwaffe. When the bombing raids were at their height, every night, usually after 9pm, the sirens would go and those not heading for air raid shelters would anxiously scan skies criss-crossed by searchlights as Heinkel and Junkers aircraft droned overhead. It was a nerve-racking time for all concerned. The threat was real. Motherwell Bridge, in common with all major factories, had to construct its own air raid shelters within its grounds. Although few bombs were to fall in earnest, Motherwell's A.R.P. and Home Guard units regularly made the journey through to Clydebank to aid that stricken town, which was to suffer more than 1,000 casualties. Motherwell, itself, opened its

doors to hundreds of Clydeside refugees bombed out of their homes. The stories of carnage and quiet heroism were legion.

Wartime precautions were strictly observed in Lanarkshire, owing to its importance to the war effort. Works like Motherwell Bridge sent roof watchers on training courses, and the Home Guard underwent weapons training and target practice. It has to be said, however, that Motherwell Bridge's platoon, E Company, was less than enthusiastic about its duties.

**MACHINE SHOP STAFF.** A photograph taken in 1950 of the machine shop staff.

# CHAPTER 6

Mr Masterton, who as Lieutenant was the officer in charge of the platoon, was constantly having to chivvy them into attendance of Sunday and Wednesday drill parades and other activities. Of the optimum complement of 79 men, the normal platoon strength ran to about 40 - and of these only a little more than half ever turned out. Lieutenant Masterton, an inveterate keeper of lists and records, notes grimly: "Men available - 39. On parade - 2 officers and 13 men. Absent - 24. Of this 24, four notified a Sergeant that they would not be on parade, one is now forward for prosecution and one is dodging with a supposed damaged leg."

The excuses listed for non-attendance were varied and artful - "Missed two weeks owing to marriage;" "Strained knee, not even playing football. Requires to be massaged on Wednesdays (parade nights);" "Has skin disease and can't wear Home Guard clothes ... this man looks quite healthy;" "Working long hours and wife ill." Even in the matter of holding onto their equipment, the Motherwell Bridge platoon wasn't terribly efficient. Lieutenant Masterton lists as lost, five pairs of gloves, three tin helmets, one waist belt, one cap badge and three oil bottles (for lubricating weapons). However, the company secretary gamely shepherded his awkward squad round special drills in the use of grenades, rifles and other military manoeuvres. In the war years, the spirit of TV's Captain Mainwaring most definitely lived.

It was, however, a security conscious time. Buses, operating a curtailed service to conserve fuel, drove with blinds down on the passenger windows. Car headlights were masked with paper to allow out only a glimmer of light and of course there was no street lighting - itself a regular cause of casualties as people bumped into lamp posts or were knocked down by vehicles in the darkness. Wardens did the rounds, checking that black-out curtains were in place, and offenders who breached the regulations were fined. Later on, travel restrictions on buses became even tighter, with only war workers and return ticket holders being allowed to travel after 10.30pm at weekends.

As rationing began to bite and shortages grew, queues for everything from public transport to provisions became a regular part of life in Motherwell, a town already bursting at the seams with refugees and servicemen recuperating from injuries. It is perhaps not widely

EGYPTIAN CONTRACT. Sections being assembled in the workshops during 1930 for the Egyptian State Railways Mallahet-El-Hadra subway.

known, but the authorities actually took people to court for queue-jumping. One Motherwell man - and he was by no means the only one - was fined £1, with the alternative of five days' imprisonment, for trying to bypass a queue for a bus.

All through the war, at Motherwell Bridge, the glass skylights on the roof of the works were painted black in compliance with black-out regulations. Security was also tight. As far back as April, 1938, the company had received a visit at its London office from a senior Royal Navy intelligence officer warning them that it had drawn up a black list of suspect individuals who might attempt to find work at firms carrying out Government and Admiralty contracts. The men were suspected of being

WARTIME WELDERS. Top: Some of the woman welders at the works during the second world war.
Bottom: Back row from left - Ina Thompson, Sadie Campbell (became Mrs Joe Nelson), Claire Renwick, Cath Riley (became Mrs Eddie Doyle), Cathy Blair (became Mrs Robert Meek).
Front row from left - Ann Stevenson, Mary Russell (became Mrs Jimmy McPheat), Sarah Bracken, Mattie Greer (became Mrs Bunny Wasson).

unimpressed. He dutifully reported to head office that he had received "under double cover" (i.e. a sealed envelope inside another sealed envelope) a communication saying a Commander from Naval Intelligence would be calling on them. His report on the visit itself was a model of brevity. The intelligence officer had obviously played his cards so close to his chest as to be almost unintelligible. After detailing "what he could gather" were the Navy's concerns about keeping an eye open for suspicious characters, Pettigrew commented: "Beyond this, the Commander had very little to tell us except that it was absolutely necessary the matter should be kept secret."

Fostered by security conscious services, the spectres of saboteurs and Fifth Columnists were wartime's 'bogeymen.' They loomed much larger in the public's imagination than they did in reality. What the scares did achieve was to make the hiring of foreign nationals in Britain extremely difficult. The 'red tape' involved was enormous. When Motherwell Bridge was asked by one of its clients to take on a Chinese engineering student, Wah Hing Ng, for work experience it spawned a spate of official clearances and lengthy correspondence which seemed to involve everyone from the Home Office mandarins to the works managing director downwards before permission eventually was granted.

Even T. R. Miller had to submit his company's annual report to shareholders to an official Government censor for clearance. But if bureaucracy was rife it was a small price to pay. Once again Motherwell Bridge was booming. The works were in full production, working day and night. A 47-hour night shift, suspended in the early thirties because of lack of orders, was reintroduced. The men worked from 9.00pm to 7.30am, with two half-hour breaks for meals. The dayshift worked 47 hours a week, from 7.45am to 5.15pm, with a daily meal-break of 57 minutes - a curious figure, the origin of which remains shrouded in mystery. It was later to be rounded up to the full hour, when to comply with the 1937 Factories Act, the company changed it. At the same time it changed the dayshift to a straight 12-hour shift, from 7.45am to 7.45pm, with a one-hour lunch break and a 20-minute dinner break from 5.18 to 5.38pm. But there must somewhere lie a historical explanation for those 57 minutes - nothing which T.R. Miller or the company did was without a practical reason.

involved in industrial espionage or sabotage for foreign powers. According to the officer, Motherwell Bridge would be notified if anyone from the black list was working for the company - and if they were, a careful watch was to be kept on them by the firm. The company was also told to notify the intelligence service about any employee behaving suspiciously.

The cloak and dagger episode left Motherwell Bridge's new London manager Mr William Pettigrew singularly

Within its industrial sector, Motherwell Bridge wasn't regarded as the highest wage payer, but it was far from being the worst, and enjoyed great loyalty from its workforce; son would follow father, nephew would follow uncle, into its employ. Whole generations of families grew up and prospered on wage packets earned within Motherwell Bridge. A popular saying among local families in the thirties and forties was: "Motherwell Bridge are no' the best payers, but the work is aye steady."

Continuity of employment, for all of us, is important. Down the years that has most certainly been a feature of Motherwell Bridge. It still has a surprisingly large number of personnel, from shop floor to management, who have spent 30 to 40 years in its employ - a refreshing permanence in a world where company loyalty to employees is very largely regarded as a quaint anachronism.

The full employment of the war years was all a far cry from the Hungry Thirties, the first five years of which T.R. Miller described as the worst trading conditions ever encountered by Motherwell Bridge in its history. As orders dwindled, even the famed Wiggins roof failed to cushion the company against the rough edges of depression as oil companies were forced to put on hold plant improvement and expansion plans. The orders for Wiggins roofs, which in 1934 totalled 29, dropped to two in the following year. At the works, the nightshift had to be discontinued and men laid off. It was a time of great financial uncertainty. Even so, Motherwell Bridge still managed to turn in profits, year on year, although there was precious little meat on the bones of domestic contracts.

Indeed, if the company had not worked assiduously at gaining overseas sales, it would have been in an infinitely more parlous financial situation. Writing to a disgruntled shareholder, Patrick Alston, son of the late company chairman, John Alston, who died in 1934, T.R Miller,

# WHEN HITLER PLAYED CUPID...

DURING the Second World War about 40 young women were employed on the shop floor at Motherwell Bridge to release men for active service. Among the very first batch of six girls to be employed at the works in December, 1941, were 20-year-old Marcina Dunne and her older sister, Bridie, whose husband was in the army. A cinema cashier at the Roxy in Hamilton, Marcina started at Motherwell Bridge as a crane driver. It wasn't long, though, before she was transferred to another section to train as a driller - under the man she was later to marry, Charlie Higgins.

In all, about eight couples met their life partners inside the gates of Motherwell Bridge. Charlie and Marcina were one of the first couples to wed. They walked down the aisle of St. Mary's R.C. Church, Hamilton, in 1942.

Marcina worked at Motherwell Bridge for 18 months before leaving to have her first of seven children. Charlie, now aged 80, did a little better. He was with Motherwell Bridge for 46 years, from 1935 to 1981, having joined the company at the age of 19. The family connection with Motherwell Bridge doesn't end there, though. Charlie's second eldest son learned his trade at the Bridge Works. Another son, Joe, and one of his grandsons, Gavin, currently work with the company.

While the first day at Motherwell Bridge was obviously a little daunting, Marcina says she and the other girls were very well treated by the men.

Another couple who met at Motherwell Bridge and later married were Colin and Margaret Ronald, who now live in Wishaw. Colin, until his retiral, worked extensively abroad for the company. Latterly he headed international sales and was awarded the MBE for services to industry.

Charlie Higgins and Marcina Dunne at their wedding in 1942.

in response to his queries over the company accounts, revealed that the "handsome profit" of £8,500 returned for the year of 1934 was due entirely to a single large contract in Palestine. The previous year, also, the company had been reliant on an order of storage tanks from Haifa to keep the works in production. The large profits earned from that job enabled it to book in work at less than cost to keep men in employment and the plant in full operation, returning a small profit for the year. Unlike many of its competitors, Motherwell Bridge financed its cut-price deals from its own resources.

The years 1930 to 1935 saw Motherwell Bridge embark upon many foreign contracts as it tried to weather the depression: a bridge for the Egyptian State; oil tanks for Burma; a trade mission to Russia; contracts within New Zealand, South Africa, Iraq (an important 'first'), Palestine, Syria and India. Even a trade mission to China was undertaken and an agency set up (later to be discontinued because of the war in China). In India, also, there were new problems - heavy import tax on fabricated steel. Combined with freight charges, it put the company at huge disadvantage when tendering against fabricators already based upon the sub-continent, and getting their steel locally. Motherwell Bridge's steel prices, at £4 10s (£4.50p) extra per ton, were fully one third higher than local steel prices. It was the reason it lost out on a major contract containing £180,000 worth of tonnage - a difference of some £60,000 on local prices.

However, 1936 saw the long-running depression finally bottom out, with the company still in much better shape than many of its competitors to respond quickly to the upturn in business. Throughout the lean years it had always placed a high priority on keeping its plant in top condition, modernising whenever it was financially feasible. For the year of 1936 Motherwell Bridge returned record profits of £30,000 as domestic price margins at long last improved. In 1937, despite major steel shortages, profits returned were still buoyant, there having been an upsurge of 70 per cent in orders for Wiggins roofs. On Christmas Eve of that year the Board played Santa Claus and voted to give each member of the office staff a bonus amounting to 10 per cent of their yearly salary as reward for their services during what had been a "strenuous year". It was a bonus which was to be repeated a couple of years later, to be followed in 1939 with the establishment of the company's first staff pensions scheme.

## BOMBED OUT FOUR TIMES

LONDON office manager William Pettigrew was less fortunate than Motherwell Bridge when it came to avoiding German bombing raids. His home was damaged four times by exploding bombs, which smashed windows, brought down ceilings and demolished part of the brickwork. On one occasion the force of the blast sent him flying into his air raid shelter. For much of the war, Mr Pettigrew and his wife were confined to two barely habitable rooms within their bomb-damaged home.

Part of the 1936 upsurge in trade was an increasing tranche of armaments contracts. In Europe the forces of Fascism were gathering in Germany, Italy, Spain and Portugal, while other nations flirted with the movement. Whatever was being said in public, a nervous Britain was gearing up its armaments production. In Berlin, having watched Herr Hitler stage the Olympic Games as an exhibition of German triumphalism to show the world he was fashioning a Nazi Third Reich that would endure for a thousand years, few observers were under any illusion that war was far distant. Once again the need would be for fuel storage depots, aeroplane hangars, shipping, armaments and all the accoutrements of war.

Even so, according to its financial report for 1938, another year of record profitability, Motherwell Bridge was not overly reliant upon armed services contracts for its financial returns. At its annual general meeting the company stated: "From the trading point of view, the year was the most favourable experienced in the history of the company. Due in large measure to the effect of the Government's rearmament programme, competition for business was less severe, so with adequate steel supplies output reached record levels. A large proportion of the output again consisted of tank work on which satisfactory profits were earned. Government orders represented a relatively small part of the output, and as prices are strictly controlled they did not augment the profits to any appreciable extent."

In some respects, it was a slightly disingenuous statement. There can be little question that the ratcheting up of the British war effort manifested itself in a general improvement of the economy; any large injection of Government cash in industry breeds many spin-offs. In 1938, too, Motherwell Bridge, in common with other major businesses, pledged its support to the great Empire Exhibition staged at Bellahouston in Glasgow - an international event, which as well as being a most wonderful spectacle, was also designed to remind a land-hungry Germany that the British Empire was still at the zenith of its powers in terms of technology, science and resources, making it a formidable foe in the event of it ever being attacked. Motherwell Bridge went guarantor for the sum of £500 towards the cost of staging the Exhibition - and at its conclusion, when its financial affairs were wound up, were even refunded a proportion of that cash, a perhaps salutary reminder to modern-day events organisers that it is possible to stage the greatest spectacle of the era, and still balance the books.

**NEW CRANE GANTRY.**
The new crane gantry at the south end of the works being finished utilising the already installed five-ton crane.
The gantry was 422 feet long by 28 feet high with rail centres at 25 feet. When finished the gantry had two cranes, a five-ton capacity at 120 feet radius and a 10-ton at 62 feet radius.
The gantry was the largest all-welded structure in Europe at the time and was completed by 1939.
The cranes were supplied by Babcock and Wilcox (Dalmuir) and were said to be originally intended for Dieppe harbour but export was vetoed by the Government because of prospective hostilities in Europe.

That same year, too, Motherwell Bridge made one of its most lucrative business deals. It joined a consortium of fabricating firms to form Bellman Hangars Ltd. to manufacture transportable aircraft hangars, principally for export abroad. Made in sections and very light, the hangars could be easily erected or dismantled and transported to forward war areas. They were used extensively by the RAF and the Army also used them to keep stores under cover. Within one year of the consortium starting up, the new company had received orders for hangars which totalled in value more than £2 million - an enormous sum, even when split among the partners.

For the wartime workers at Motherwell Bridge, life was hard, but rewarding. On the shop floor, men over 21 received what was known as a war advance of £1 a week, on top of their wages. Pay day at the time was a Tuesday, their weekly wages being calculated from the Wednesday of the previous week. Conditions within the bays were not as they are today. They were huge, draughty sheds which could be abominably cold in winter. The only form of heating were the small furnaces used to heat the rivets red hot (welding was still in its infancy) and from time to time workers would slip over to warm themselves briefly before continuing their tasks. Given those conditions, it was perhaps not surprising that T.R. used to don his special overcoat with its deep fur lining when making his tours of inspection.

BELOW: GANTRY GIRDER JIG. One of the jigs designed and produced by the company for welding gantry girders to be used on the new gantry at the south end of the works in the late 1930s. The size of the sections within the jig can best be imagined by comparing the size of the two personnel against the jig.

# NEW BATTLE OF THE BOYNE

IN the 1930s Motherwell Bridge found itself embroiled in a new Battle of the Boyne over completion of a viaduct bridge in Ireland. The company had undertaken the contract for the Great Northern Railway (Ireland) Company, sub-letting the construction of it to another firm. But it went bankrupt, forcing Motherwell Bridge to step in and complete the contract.

The change-over and other delays caused the railway company to invoke penalty clauses, paying Motherwell Bridge a substantially reduced fee. As the company troubleshooter, T.R. Miller went over to Dublin, where he was successful in reducing the penalty period under dispute by five months. Unable to claim against the insolvent sub-contractor, Motherwell Bridge considered going to law to have the financial penalties reduced still further. On legal advice, they dropped the idea. However, there were no hard feelings.

To commemorate its completion Motherwell Bridge had special books of matches made, featuring pictures of the bridge, and nicely encased in a specially engraved pewter holder.

THE CENTRE SPAN for the Boyne Viaduct at Drogheda under trial erection during 1931 at rear of the Motherwell Bridge Works.

THE OLD VIADUCT was completed in 1855 and remained in service until June 1932.

THE NEW BOYNE VIADUCT was finally completed in November 1932. The new bridge was built within the old wrought iron structure and the old spans removed.

CHAPTER 6

The coat, itself, almost came to a sad end.
His housekeeper, taking a dislike to it, threw it out.
An incandescent T.R., when he discovered its
disappearance, ordered its recovery from the municipal
dump. It was duly found and returned to its fond owner -
and to this day remains as a piece of Motherwell Bridge
memorabilia in the Glasgow home of one of T.R.'s
grandsons, Peter Fleming-Brown.

The coat had a more chequered history than most people
realise. Originally a wedding present from his in-laws, the
coat was a "driving coat". Its lining was musquash, most
suitable as a protection from the elements when out in a
horse-drawn carriage. The original exterior fabric was
replaced by T.R. with clerical gabardine when it became
worn.

Among the most important contracts undertaken by
Motherwell Bridge during the war years was the
construction, from start to finish, of two types of troop
landing craft for the armed services, which saw action on
D-Day and in the Mediterranean. The fabrication was
done at the Motherwell works, where the shop floor
complement was stepped up to 700, but the craft were
actually built at Forthbank shipyard, Alloa, which was
specially acquired by the Admiralty in 1941. The laying
down of a complete shipyard was done by Motherwell
Bridge. At the shipyard special rail sidings were
constructed to facilitate transport of material from
Motherwell. The Alloa shipbuilding operation was run for
the company by Mr Thomas Ness, remaining in full
production until September, 1945, when it was
decommissioned by the Admiralty. Throughout the war
Forthbank employed a workforce of around 500,
including 100 women.

Over that period it constructed a total of 54 Mark IV
LCTs, at its peak producing one vessel a fortnight. The
craft, 186 feet long, 40 feet wide, and with a draft of just
3 feet at the bow, were used in the Mediterranean in 1942
and in the D-Day landings of 1944. The company also built
two larger Mark VIII LCTs for use in tropical conditions.
Larger than the Mark IVs, they were 225 feet in length,
and 38 feet wide, with a draft at the front of just under
5 feet. With the cessation of hostilities, another 10 which
were to be built were cancelled by the Admiralty.

All in all, Motherwell Bridge constructed £2 million
worth of landing craft. The work accounted for some 64

## TR's Sign Made Railmen See Red

T.R. MILLER never lost an opportunity to publicise
Motherwell Bridge. Because the plant bordered the
main Glasgow-London railway, in 1938 he had a large
red neon sign, emblazoning the company name,
installed alongside the track so that passengers could
see it as they whisked past.

However, the London, Midland and Scottish Railway
Company was none too pleased. It wrote to the
company complaining that the red sign was a potential
hazard to train drivers who might mistake it as a
danger signal from the nearby Lesmahagow junction
box and ram on the emergency brakes. After several
consultations, T.R. changed the lettering from red to
gold, much to the satisfaction of the railway company.

per cent of the company's total output.

Taking on a shipbuilding role, for the company, was not
an easy assignment. Although in Mr Ness it had
appointed an experienced shipbuilder, Motherwell Bridge
was new to the industry. Production at times was hit by a
series of industrial demarcation disputes and man
management problems. Indeed, the yard received a
'rocket' from the Admiralty about the frequency with
which it found itself being called in to adjudicate on
issues. However, by the end of the war, the company
received from their Lordships a letter expressing their
appreciation for services rendered to the Allied Cause in
building up the Combined Operations fleet. It talked of
the "novel methods" employed in the construction of the
craft, and concluded: "The unconditional surrender of the
enemy has led to the cancellation of the last of your naval
orders but Their Lordships, in thanking you for a notable
achievement, hope that the happy spirit of co-operation
between yourselves and the Navy will continue."

Motherwell Bridge also constructed the famed floating
Bailey Bridges (invented by Sir Donald Bailey) used to
ford rivers during the Allied advance across Europe.
The portable bridges, capable of supporting vehicles, were
one of the most important military logistical tools in
getting men and materiel to the Front as a retreating
enemy blew up conventional bridges to hamper the Allied
thrust forward.

MAIN PICTURE: LANDING CRAFT SHIPYARD. Two Mark VIII landing craft under construction at the Motherwell Bridge shipyard at Forthbank, Alloa with number 4088 nearest. Number 4087 was launched on 22nd October 1945 and towed to Rosyth the same day. Number 4088 was dismantled on its berth and the order for the remaining six mark VIIIs was cancelled due to the end of the war. LCTs 4085 and 4086 were the only Mark VIIIs to be handed over.
INSET TOP: FORTHBANK. General view of the company's landing craft shipyard at Forthbank, Alloa.
INSET BELOW: MARK VIII LANDING CRAFT. LCT 4086 on the River Forth after acceptance by the Royal Navy.

INSET: LANDING CRAFT. Bow of Mark VIII number 4088 showing riveting detail with a nearly completed Mark VIII visible in the dock in the background.

# LCT 1345's LAST NAVY VOYAGE

### By Lieut. J. Ian Ballantyne, RNVR (Retired)

SHIPS weave an eternal fascination on the imagination. But often the men and women who build them watch them disappear down the slipway into oblivion. Unless the vessel is well-known or features in some unusual incident, they never learn what kind of sea-going ship they have constructed, how she was regarded by the men who sailed her, or what voyages she made. That was to be the fate of most of the landing craft made by Motherwell Bridge during the war years at Alloa.

However, sometimes the veil lifts. The following is an account of the first voyage of the Motherwell Bridge-built LCT 1345. It and a sister ship, 1346, were specially designed to see service in the tropics. It never ever happened, as retired RNVR officer Ian Ballantyne records in his recollections of 1345's one

**LIEUTENANT IAN BALLANTYNE**
(Lt. Ballantyne is now a retired architect living near Inverness)

and only voyage as a Royal Navy vessel under his command. He writes:

"In the early days of 1945 you would have found me, a young sub-Lieutenant H.O. (Hostilities Only), RNVR, at a shore base in Westcliffe-on-Sea, officially 'resting' following many months of strenuous operations in the English Channel. I was contemplating a return to general service, with a possible posting to the Far East where the war with

Japan was nearing a climax - so it was with surprise and some disappointment that I received quite different orders to proceed to Alloa to commission and command LCT 1345.

"She was shored up in a small dry-dock, and in the adjacent dock, stern towards the entrance lock, was her sister ship LCT 1346, some few months behind in the building programme. I had the impression, mistaken of course, that the beam of the boat was wider than the lock and was apprehensive about going out stern first under main engines without scraping the new paintwork. But the foreman shipbuilder reassured me there was 6 inches to spare each side, and that in any case a pilot would be taking us downstream to Bo'ness.

"I had not previously been appointed to a newly built boat,

LCT FLOTILLA. Part of Lieutenant Ballantyne's flotilla of LCTs at St Mawes, Cornwall in 1945 showing Motherwell Bridge built landing craft 1344 and 1345. These were among the last Mark IVs built by the company. The very last was number 1346 which never joined Lieutenant Ballantyne's flotilla but according to company records was handed over to the Admiralty on 6th July 1945.

**THE CREW OF LCT 1345.**
Ship's company of landing craft LCT 1345 at St Mawes in 1945.

and I have to say she looked really handsome, impressively sturdy and seaworthy - and, for a landing craft, surprisingly elegant. My mild disappointment at my posting to a large extent was assuaged. While the boat was being completed I was billeted with the local police sergeant and his wife, a short walk from the dockyard, and I spent the first week familiarising myself with the boat and the manuals and talking to the builders about various aspects of construction and performance. Mark 4s were well known to me. I had served on one years earlier in Scapa Flow as a First Lieutenant and had commanded a Mark 4 in the English Channel the previous year. My main interest was to ascertain how this boat, having been adapted for tropical service, differed from the others.

"She appeared to be longer, and therefore heavier; she was fitted with deck awnings to the bridge, after-deck and tank-hold, and, if I recall correctly, air-conditioning was installed in the wheelhouse, the chartroom, the wardroom and below deck in the crew's mess deck and engine room. Less welcome, though, was the fact that she was fitted with two diesel main engines with starboard turning screws. These gave LCTs their characteristic crab-like gait in the water and made ship handling at close quarters extremely tricky.

"The early days in the life of a new ship and crew are designated as 'shake-down,' but in truth they are more of a 'shake up.'

There is the crew to organise, watches to be arranged, ship's records initiated (deck logs, engine room logs, ammunition and stores inventories, wine and rum records, pay records and accounts); equipment to be checked and stowed; ropes, line and tackle checked; main and auxiliary engines, winches, capstan, pumps and telegraphs to be tested; tools checked, fire hoses and life-saving equipment tested; charts organised and corrected; signal flags and lamps checked and stowed; armaments checked (but not fired); water and fuel taken on. It is a welter of duties during which the C.O. and First Lieutenant weigh up the crew, the crew weigh up the officers and each other, and gradually some sense of order is established. These tasks accomplished, I signed for the ship. We ceremonially hoisted our pristine White Ensign and were ready to leave.

"The pilot took us, main engines half astern, through the lock as clean as a whistle. He had my admiration and I told him so,

and he assured me I'd soon get the hang of it. But I felt his nervousness as we approached Bo'ness Harbour, our first destination 12 miles downstream. The entrance to the outer harbour basin was narrow and at right angles to the flow of the river. When the pilot ordered, "Fenders, port side!" I knew he was concerned. We bumped our way in but without damage and a second right-angled turn took us into the inner basin and a mooring alongside the quay. Only then did he admit, 'This wee harbour's a right bugger - even for me.' He left us immediately, reassuring me that it was a lot easier to get out than in.

"We stayed at Bo'ness for two or three days and were glad to be under way again. The local cinema had been burned down the previous month, the harbour area was dominated by a huge black coal bing, and there was only one understocked pub nearby. The army had a shooting range on the edge of town and I organised some practice for the crew, otherwise we fretted to be on our way to the Naval base at Rosyth eight miles down river.

"At Rosyth our sailing orders were to proceed to Devonport in the English Channel, at this stage of the war unescorted, as the North Sea was no longer considered risky. The eastern seaboard was unfamiliar to me but the voyage was uneventful, the sea calm and the sea lanes quiet. The nights were dark as pitch. We navigated by 'pilotage,' compass azimuth fixes on the headland lighthouses and light ships, past Bass Rock, St. Abb's Head, Farne Islands, Tynemouth, Flamborough Head, Great Yarmouth and Harwich to North Foreland off the south estuary of the Thames, through the treacherous Goodwin Sands and into the busy sea-lanes of the Straits of Dover. The passage through the Strait was slow and tedious and our maximum speed barely exceeded the fierce rate of the tidal race. The seawall at Dover seemed to be off our starboard quarter for an entire morning watch.

"Thereafter we were in familiar waters, by Beachy Head, Selsey Bill, Isle of Wight, and the great buoy off St. Catherine's Point which had been the rendezvous for all the cross-channel convoys to France. We crossed the path of convoys still on passage southward, but by now the front line had moved into Germany. Continuing on by the Needles, Portland Bill, past Start Point towards Eddystone Light and north into Plymouth Sound, the Port Signal Station directed us to proceed to the inner dockyard at Devonport and secure alongside the ships of our flotilla already in harbour. When the telegraphs conveyed my order, "Finished with main engines" to the engine room barely ten days had passed since we had left Alloa. Although I did not know it at the time, LCT 1345 had completed her first and last long sea voyage. Her story, however, was not complete.

"On reporting to the Flotilla Officer I learned the answer to many questions which I urgently needed to settle the anxieties of the crew, who never cared to be kept in the dark too long. We learned the flotilla's destination was the Combined Operations base at Cochin in Madras State, South West India. The flotilla was to be transported there on victory ships, the LCTs spot-welded to the decks. The crew took the news well and we settled in to a lengthy period of waiting, known in navy-speak as 'swinging round the buoy'. It was always a particularly volatile time for morale and discipline, calling for inventive diversion. "Because the ship was new we were denied the usual ploy of painting ship. The situation was relieved by an event we could not readily have invented - the sudden end to the war in Europe, culminating in VE Day on May 8, 1945.

The mainbrace was spliced on Admiralty orders (frequently), flags flew from every halyard and we fired off every cartridge in our signal locker. They were expensive, and on my chit, but in the circumstances I expected to be - and was - excused the profligacy. Within a few days, though, we were back to the waiting game - and by this time we had been told there was little likelihood of the flotilla going to India.

"Still maintaining a state of readiness, we proceeded to a new anchorage at Carrick Roads, off St. Mawes, near Falmouth. Another period of enforced idleness threw up once more the need for distraction and some absorbing activities. Ours proved to be already there in the shape of a crippled fleet destroyer stranded on a beach a few cable lengths from our moorings. I had no authority to do so, but a

LCTs 1344 and 1345 moored to a buoy at St Mawes, Cornwall.

AT EASE. Close up of landing craft 1345 showing some of the ship's armaments.

compulsion to board her persisted and on an idle afternoon I rowed over and with some difficulty climbed the after mooring hawser onto her quarter-deck. Despite being holed for'ard by a mine or torpedo, the destroyer, of pre-war construction, proved a cornucopia of excellent fittings and furnishings.

"A request to refurbish our own vessel with the fittings being surprisingly granted, we set to work. I appointed myself as ship's carpenter (chippy) and stripped out our somewhat utilitarian chart room, refitting it with a new chart table and drawers in beautiful Honduras mahogany, all with highly polished brass handles. With the help of the signalman we also constructed a new signal bridge abaft the funnel to permit line-astern signalling, and to the especial delight of the Coxswain and P.O. motor mechanic I built them each a fully-outfitted cabin in the wings of the tank-crew

quarters. When all was done 1345 must have been the smartest, best equipped and most comfortable LCT that ever floated.

"At midnight on August 14 I was wakened by a deck watchman, so excited he could hardly speak, to say the war was over; he had just heard it announced by the Prime Minister on the radio. A few days later the commanding officers were called to a briefing by the Flotilla Commander and it was made clear the flotilla was no longer needed for India. Shortly afterwards the flotilla was ordered to proceed to Appledore in North Devon for decommissioning. We sailed there independently, south and west, by Lizard Point and Longship Light off Land's End, northwards by Trevose Head and Hartland Point to Barnstaple Bay and a rendezvous at the huge bell buoy east of Lundy Island at the entrance to the Bristol Channel. The approaches to Appledore

Harbour are treacherous, with access possible for only two hours on each side of high water (the tidal rise and fall is the highest in England). The leading craft took on a pilot who took us in on a zig-zag course along the buoyed channel into harbour.

"The regulation period for 'paying off' a Mark 4 was ten days but from previous experience I knew that, if well organised, decommissioning could be completed in four or five days. An undertaking to add any days saved to their statutory 14 days' leave was all the incentive the crew needed. The tasks were completed within five days and the crew left on their extended leave prior to reporting to their depots.

"I, too, left her, mothballed and secured to a buoy midstream in the River Taw at high tide, knowing that within a few hours she would be ignominiously settled in the estuarial mud of a fast-ebbing tide. Her builders had given us a sound and seaworthy vessel, and as a result of our additional labours, she was an exceptional and unique boat, although never called upon to fulfil the role for which she was built. I have often wondered her fate. Did she go meekly to a breaker's yard or is she perhaps even today plying to and fro as a river ferry in some distant corner of the world? She had been my responsibility and my home for many months - and you never forget a house where you have lived or a ship in which you have sailed."

They were tested out on the River Calder in Lanarkshire before dispatch. One by one, sections were attached and the bridge extended across its full width.

As part of its war effort, Motherwell Bridge also extended its works premises and installed new cranes. It also put in a new smithy, incorporating in it its first custom-built welding bay, at a total cost of more than £40,000. While the works was in constant full production, the war years also incurred heavy taxation of 50 per cent on company profits. Motherwell Bridge was also expected to invest heavily in Government money-raising exercises such as the issue of War Bonds (for a Glasgow Weapons Week it invested £10,000 in Bonds). For workers, too, any increase in earnings tended to be swallowed up by rising prices. Within a year of the outbreak of war, the cost of living index had jumped by 24 per cent.

While the war dominated the company's activities, there were civilian matters to attend to as well. In 1941 T.R.'s son, Alexander Ronald - the second A.R. - who worked with the company was invited to join the Board of Directors. He was then in his 25th year. However, within months of his appointment being ratified at the company's annual general meeting, he joined the Royal Engineers and was eventually posted to India. It was agreed by the Board to continue paying him his full salary until he obtained a commission - at which point the matter would be reviewed. In 1944, when he attained the rank of captain, the Board agreed to continue his annual allowance of £369 10s (£369.50p) for another year.

The arrival of A.R. Miller as director was not the only Boardroom change. Since the death of John Alston in 1934, the company had been operating without a

# CHURCHILL'S SECRET WEAPON

MOTHERWELL Bridge was one of six Scottish firms involved in making Winston Churchill's secret weapon for the Normandy landings in 1944 - the Mulberry artificial harbours. Towed across the English Channel and assembled on the other side in time for the opening of the Second Front, they were designed to permit ships of any size to quickly disembark troops irrespective of tides.

Blockships, floating breakwaters, piers and pierheads were used. Thousands of scientists, engineers and technicians worked for many months on the top-secret project, code-named Mulberry. A total of 146 concrete caissons were made. In Scotland, sections were assembled in Leith Harbour.

Writing to Stalin on June 7 -

the day after D Day - Churchill said: "Most especially secret: We are planning to construct very quickly two large synthetic harbours on the wide, sandy bay of the Seine estuary. Nothing like this has ever been seen before. Great ocean liners will be able to discharge and run by numerous piers supplies to the fighting troops. This must be quite unexpected by the enemy and will enable the build-up to proceed with very great independence of weather conditions."

The wartime Premier however, had under-estimated the ferocity of the elements. The sections were towed across the Channel, itself a considerable feat, and assembled. But a four-day gale, the worst in 40 years, wreaked havoc. One artificial harbour was

wrecked, but its salvageable sections were used to repair the second harbour at Arromanches, ten miles away. Arromanches became the principal landing point of men and materiel for the invasion.

The other companies working with Motherwell Bridge on Operation Mulberry were Alexander Findlay & Co. Ltd, of Motherwell, Sir William Arrol & Co, and P. & W. McLellan Ltd. The prefabrication working drawings were supplied by Redpath, Brown & Co. Heavily involved in the design of the concrete structures of the floating harbour was Sir Malcolm McAlpine, of Sir Robert McAlpine & Sons. The pierheads were designed by Clyde shipbuilder Henry Pearson Lobnitz, of Renfrew company Lobnitz & Co.

SOCIAL CLUB PRESENTATIONS. Alexander Ronald Miller presenting racing pigeon trophies to Bobby Muir (left) and Sanny Bulloch (right) in the company's Social and Recreation Club during 1949.

ROBERT McGAW
Joined Motherwell Bridge in 1904 at the age of 14 as an office boy and was with the company until his death in 1953 when he was chief wages clerk.

chairman. In 1942 T.R. Miller was formally elected to the position. Making him chairman as well as managing director was no more than regularising a situation which, for all practical purposes, already existed. Since his close friend John Alston died, T.R. had assumed those duties which normally fell to a company chairman: he was the company.

In late 1943, it seemed a turning point in the hostilities was being reached. There was talk of a Second Front being opened up; mobile blood units went round major Lanarkshire companies, including Motherwell Bridge, seeking donors. There were plenty of volunteers. Even the intrepid T.R. must have been convinced victory was not too far distant because in October of that year he returned to the War Department his personal automatic .32 Webber & Scott pistol, along with 67 rounds of ammunition. In fact, he - and the company - were already looking forward to the post-war years and new trading partners.

By November of 1943 the company was involved in talks with the Anglo-Iranian Oil Company about being appointed sole supplier of oil storage tanks in Persia. The first order placed with Motherwell Bridge was for the construction

of a total of 25 large tanks, 17 of them with Wiggins roofs - a truly exceptional order. It was of such magnitude that before Motherwell Bridge could take it on, it had to obtain guarantees from Colvilles that it would receive 30,000 tons of steel for each of the first three post-war years to fulfil the contract. T.R. personally negotiated the steel requirements with Sir John Craig, of Colvilles, late in 1944.

The war in Europe was entering its final phase. The future for the company looked secure, having gained an enormous contract which would more than take up the slack as the war contracts wound down. There was plenty to sing about. In fact, that was precisely what the company did, to the whole of Scotland.

It was selected to represent the nation on the fourth anniversary of the regular BBC radio programme, Works Wonders, an entertainment series similar to the very popular Workers' Playtime. A mixed choir from the company went on the air to sing a choral version of The Isle of Mull.

It wasn't too long, either, before the rest of Motherwell - and indeed much of the free world - was celebrating in earnest. In September of that year a huge crowd gathered at Motherwell Cross to cheer as the town's lights were switched back on. It was still a modified form of lighting - more of a 'dim out' as opposed to a black-out, but it was a ray of optimism in austerity Britain. Weather reports were no longer censored, being only a couple of days old compared to ten. Dances were allowed to continue until 11.30pm. Saving alerts, there was a general relaxation of many of the wartime regulations. Better times lay, as ever, just tantalisingly around the corner.

# A JEWEL OF A LAW CASE

A COURT case over a flawed jewel and potential litigation over the breakdown of a 1,000 ton press at Motherwell Bridge don't seem to have anything in common. Yet in 1937 they did: legal precedent.

The directors of Motherwell Bridge wanted to sue the German manufacturers of their 1,000-ton press, which broke down in one of their busiest years, putting them to considerable expense. The company had obtained the press in 1925. Three years later defects were discovered which were traced to faulty casting. No claim was made against the German manufacturers, who suggested certain repairs, and the press was soon back in action.

But in 1936 new faults, cracks in the base again due to the faulty casting, rendered the press inoperable for a period of five weeks. It also cost a considerable sum of money to put right. Directors took legal opinion on whether the company could raise an action for damages against the manufacturers. They were told that such a step was time-barred, proceedings having to be started within six years of the cause of the problem manifesting itself.

That was where the jewel came in: a woman who had purchased a flawed jewel in 1923 had just raised an action against the seller. To get round the six-year rule, she pleaded fraud had been committed, which would have taken the action out of any time limit. However, in court she was unable to establish fraud - and immediately fell foul of the six-year time bar, losing her case. Motherwell Bridge, when it heard the result, decided not to sue the German manufacturers.

SACK PRESS The Sack 1,000 ton hydraulic press was built in Germany in 1924 and purchased by the company in 1925. A considerable amount of production time was lost, over the years, due to a faulty casting. This particular view shows a sphere plate, or petal, being pressed for the Dounreay containment sphere for the fast breeder reactor. The press in its early years was very much used for trough sections required for bridge decks and ships bulkheads.

# CHAPTER 7

# Conquering the Middle East

The passengers stepped from the plane at Basra airport, Iraq, a little stunned at the blast of furnace-like heat that enveloped them as they disembarked. For those making the journey for the first time, nothing had really prepared them for the full rigours of an Arabian summer; it was like stepping into an oven. Obediently they filed out of the airport exit gates. As they passed through, they were scrutinised by a short, stockily built man with a large, leonine head and riveting eyes that twinkled when he laughed. He was in his early forties and was wearing an atrociously loud, loose-fitting floral shirt of the kind favoured by American tourists in Hawaii. He stepped forward and introduced himself as Emile Bustani, saying:

"I understand Motherwell Bridge are forming an erection company in the Middle East. How about us teaming up?"

In that moment, the creation of Mothercat, which was to become the biggest and most successful Anglo-Arab construction and trading company in the Middle East was born. It was to go on with extreme rapidity to establish itself as a world player, handling civil and mechanical engineering contracts throughout the Middle East before extending into the Mediterranean region, India, Pakistan and many African states, in a partnership that was to endure for 17 years. In the Indo-Pakistan and Gulf regions, alone, it was to construct oil pumping stations in Iraq; build desalination plants in Kuwait producing two million gallons of fresh water a day; install prefabricated accommodation in Aden for the Air Ministry; design and construct a natural gas power plant and cooling towers at Multan, West Pakistan; install 57 miles of gas pipelines in Qatar; create roads, an airstrip and marine transportation for a wildcat oil well in Iran; carry out major pipeline construction in the Lebanon, install 28 new storage tanks at an oil terminal in Syria, and become involved in countless oil industry installations before

moving further afield with its expertise to places as far apart as Ghana and New Guinea. The new company was even to build a new Royal palace in Baghdad for the King of Iraq.

But all that lay in the future.

**EMILE BUSTANI.**
A man in a class of his own.

When Emile Bustani first held out his hand in welcome to Motherwell Bridge's Ronald Miller, who was making an extensive Middle East, India and Pakistan tour in search of new trading prospects, the year was 1949, a time when the world was still trying to get back upon an even keel after a war which had left it bedevilled with shortages of steel product needed by heavy industry to repair the shattered or badly run-down infrastructures in many former theatres of battle.

It took until April, 1950, for the new joint venture, Mothercat - short for the Motherwell Bridge Contracting and Trading Company Ltd. - to start trading. It was formally registered in February of the following year in Transjordan (later Jordan), whose legal system was based on British law, and its headquarters established in Beirut. The CAT part of the company name stood for the Contracting and Trading Company of Lebanon, which was itself a partnership of three men: Emile Bustani, its chairman; his brother-in-law Abdullah Khoury, the managing director; and Syrian-born Shukri Shammas, a London-qualified civil engineer who was head of contracts and engineering and whose speciality was advanced mathematics.

CAT was, to say the least, a colourful alliance. Shukri Shammas, as perhaps befitted a man who at one time was a teacher, was kindly, honest and home-loving, very much a family man whose house was filled with exquisite Persian rugs and happy children - to both collections of which he was constantly adding. Abdullah Khoury, a Lebanese, had spent much of his earlier life wandering through Africa on foot, participating in various expeditions. Emile Bustani, however, was in a class all

KIRKUK. The installation of incoming control manifold and spheres by Mothercat at the Kirkuk Field for Iraq Petroleum Company.

of his own: a Levant entrepreneur with a quicksilver temperament, he would frequently make lightning decisions about projects - then carry them through by sheer force of personality.

In 1951, less than four weeks before a general election, he decided to stand as a Deputy for the Lebanese Parliament. Gathering together the Bustani clan, numbering several hundred, he sent them out electioneering on his behalf and personally bombarded Beirut from the skies with pamphlets explaining his policies. Needless to say, he was elected, then went on to become one of the country's most influential politicians. Each year, at his own expense, he would bring a cross-party group of British MPs to the region to learn about Arab aspirations. He numbered as personal friends virtually every head of state and important sheikh in the region, and his opinions were canvassed by, among others, Attlee and Beaverbrook, and later Harold Macmillan, as they sought an understanding of Arab politics. In the 1950s, also, he survived an assassination attempt within the Lebanon Parliament.

Bustani's early life was no less incident-packed. Expelled from school in his native Lebanon in 1926 for agitating against the French (who then ruled Syria and Lebanon), he went to the USA, where he graduated at the Massachusetts Institute of Technology with a

Master's Degree in astro-physics. After taking a further degree, he returned to the Middle East and, with his partners, founded CAT, which grew rapidly during the war. His buccaneering personality brought numerous unconventional solutions to problems. One which conveys the essence of the man concerns a time when he was running behind schedule on a major oil pipeline contract, and in danger of incurring expensive penalty clauses. The principal hindrance was that the pipeline being constructed ran through the territory of a local tribe which had taken to frightening off the workforce by sniping at them with their ancient weapons. As the intervals between the tribe's demands for additional protection money grew shorter, and the deadline for completion grew closer, Bustani acted. He offered the local Sheikh's favourite son an aeroplane ride. Having got him on board, he kidnapped him and flew the lad to Beirut. There he got the youngster to send his father a letter saying that unless the sniping ceased, a terrible fate would befall his son. The ambushes stopped and the contract was finished on time.

Needless to say, the youngster had been in no danger, but had spent his first time out of the desert enjoying himself in the most elegant and beautiful city of the Middle East. Before sending him home, Bustani offered the youth any gift he cared to name. The lad chose a gold tooth, insisting on having one of his own perfectly healthy teeth extracted to accommodate the gold replacement.

KUWAIT. The oil and gas separators of a gathering centre built for the Kuwait Oil Company in Kuwait. These separators are just a part of the gathering centre, which includes manifolds, instruments, flow tanks, gas ducts and flares, and a pump station. This latest one includes a gas driven crude oil pump.

That, then, was the calibre of the man who, in joining forces with Motherwell Bridge through Mothercat, was to help create the most important construction trading alliance in the region. It was also to open up for Ronald Miller a career in his own right within the growth and development of Motherwell Bridge.

Being the only son of a father like T.R. Miller, a man who did not lightly relinquish control, it wasn't an easy task for the young Ronald to establish an independent role for himself within the company. He wasn't lacking in self-confidence; an English public school education at Malvern had seen to that. He had also trained in engineering companies in England, Paris and of course Chicago Bridge, the forward-looking American company with which Motherwell Bridge had forged such strong trading links. His leadership qualities were later to be rounded off by military service. Keen to see action, he had enlisted as a sapper in the Royal Engineers and rose to become a staff officer with the permanent rank of Major, serving in the Regular Indian Army. He was also the Battalion boxing champion.

Before the outbreak of war, and prior to joining the Motherwell Bridge Board of directors, Ronald had invented a new form of underground storage tank which the company, after some initial difficulties in registering, had patented in numerous countries. In trading terms, it was reasonably successful, having been adopted at several military installations. However, it didn't feature greatly in the company profile. Nevertheless, it could be regarded as a clear attempt by Ronald to 'plough his own furrow.' Immediately upon demob from the army, he was dispatched upon company business in the Middle East, inspecting sites, checking workmanship and personnel, quantifying work prospects and evaluating possible agents. He became the company's 'eyes and ears' abroad, submitting highly detailed reports back to head office on everything from regional politics to inter-company relations within the oil industry.

With the creation of Mothercat, of which he was appointed chairman, he was in his element. Having served abroad with the army, he was familiar with, and relished, the challenges of life in, to Western eyes, primitive and undeveloped regions. Like his father before him (who in the late 1930s had travelled extensively in the Middle East), he fell under its spell. Unquestionably, he was closer to Bustani, his family and the other

## THE STAMP OF SUCCESS

NOT many engineering companies have ever had their work immortalised in a special issue of commemorative stamps. But it happened in 1965 to Mothercat to mark the completion of an important pipeline contract for the Republic of Guinea. The project was a multi-million pound scheme to treble the volume of water supply to the country's capital, Conakry, which suffered acute shortages during the dry season.

Mothercat was called in to construct a pipeline through the tropical uplands from a new water source at a hydro-electric scheme, known as the Grandes Chutes. It also constructed the new reservoirs and filtration plant. When the project was completed, boosting the capital's annual water supply from 13,500 to 40,000 cubic metres, the Government issued a set of commemorative stamps in celebration.

partners than his father - although on visits to Britain Bustani would be the guest of T.R., as befitted his status as the patriarch of the business.

For Ronald the involvement with Mothercat, prior to succeeding as managing director of the company upon the death of his father in 1958, was an enjoyable - if at times hair-raising - interlude.

CAT, in addition to other sidelines unconnected with Motherwell Bridge, had its own fleet of small aircraft, including De Havillands and DC3s, to ferry personnel round the region. On one occasion in the mid-fifties, Ronald was aboard a plane which found itself flying between two ranges of mountains. Unable to rise above either, the plane was forced to make an emergency landing, upon which Ronald was promptly arrested as a suspected drug smuggler - the Lebanon being then, as now, a famed area for producing a variety of high quality hashish resin known as Lebanese Gold.

For Motherwell Bridge, the creation of Mothercat came along at exactly the right time. It neatly answered several trading requirements for Middle East business at a period when the domestic market, owing to severe shortages of steel, was still less than buoyant.

AERIAL VIEW OF KHARG ISLAND, IRAN.
Crude oil tanks and jetty are seen in the picture.

GEORGE HORTON—the Chicago
Bridge designer of the Horton Type 5
floating roof and Horton spheres.
He was a friend of T. R. Miller.

Most of the Gulf countries imposed strict rules on foreign nationals owning businesses on their soil. Outsiders were required to have an Arab partner with a major stake in any company. Just as importantly, the involvement with CAT brought on board an energetic trader who had an intimate knowledge of customs, prices and practices surrounding the hire of local labour, and the at times byzantine maze of protocol involved in doing business in largely feudal societies. Motherwell Bridge brought to the alliance technical expertise and an already firmly established reputation within the Middle East.

It also brought to the table three licensing agreements from its long-time business associate, the Chicago Bridge Company. In addition to producing and constructing Wiggins floating roofs for the oil industry's storage tanks, it was now also making under exclusive licence Hortonspheres (spherical pressure vessels, so designed because the shape guaranteed uniform stress at every point) and giant elevated water towers. Both were of considerable interest to Middle East clients - the former in the giant oil refineries, the latter in providing water at heights offering good water pressure for towns and factories.

Although not widely used in the UK, water towers were commonplace in the USA, and proved particularly suitable for the flat desert states of the Gulf.

One of the earliest contracts carried out by Mothercat was in Baghdad, where it constructed a 100 feet high water tower, with a 200,000 gallons capacity. The Iraqis insisted that because Baghdad was the third holiest city of Islam, visited by many pilgrims, the water tower had to blend in with the city's background of mosques and their high towers from which the Muezzin called the faithful to prayer.

The Motherwell Bridge towers were the most splendidly dramatic of structures, capable of being built to a height of 130 feet and of having a capacity of up to three million gallons. Despite their deceptively spindly, stilt like support legs, the structures were also capable of withstanding winds of up to 120mph - the key to their sturdiness being the careful attention paid to the design of their foundations.

A more exotic contract for Mothercat in those early years was the construction in Baghdad of a sumptuous palace for the King of Iraq. One of the great official residences of the Middle East, the Royal palace contained state conference halls, numerous Government and Royal apartments, offices and guest suites. Its great central dome was covered in Persian tiles and many of its interior rooms featured Jerusalem marble and Bethlehem limestone. It should perhaps be said that back in those Saddam-free days, Iraq was one of Britain's most loyal allies prior to, and during, the Second World War.

Nevertheless, the Middle East was then, as now, a political hot spot. In 1952, the world's greatest oil refinery at Abadan was unilaterally nationalised by Iran. It took three years for a new deal to be brokered with a consortium of eight international oil companies. However, the political uncertainties caused many refineries in the region to postpone capital expenditure as they waited to see how other Arab states would react. The nationalisation of the Suez Canal by Egypt's President Nasser, which triggered the calamitous Suez Canal invasion by Britain, was another crisis which greatly heightened Middle East tensions in the fifties. It is not widely known that Motherwell Bridge workers and other expatriates were once compulsorily bussed by the authorities to the United Arab Republic to be filmed for propaganda purposes 'greeting' Nasser's arrival at the local airport.

The assassination of King Faisal, of Saudi Arabia, was another major incident which also sent shock waves through the region as, later, did a conflict between Iraq and Syria. At times, foreign nationals found themselves subject to special restrictions. In Syria, any gathering of six people required to have a local person present to guard against foreign conspiracies. Expatriates also fell foul of other odd censorship regulations regarding some of the movies sent out for their entertainment. The authorities once decreed that a film which featured a bank raid couldn't be viewed by locals (who used to enjoy the occasional film shows immensely) in case it inspired them to mount a similar raid.

QATAR. A topping plant constructed by Mothercat at Umm Said, Qatar, for the Qatar Petroleum Company. Motherwell Bridge built the first tank in Qatar for Iraq Petroleum and it is still in operation today.

## A LITTLE TOUCH OF HOME

PROVIDING erection teams abroad with links to home was always regarded by the company as being important for morale. Motherwell Bridge used to arrange for copies of the Motherwell Times to be sent every week to every site in the UK and abroad. Sometimes, however, the arrangements fell through. During a tour of the Middle East in 1949, Ronald Miller wrote back to head office complaining that staff at Qatar were no longer receiving the weekly paper.

The failure of delivery, while a small thing in itself, was viewed seriously by the company because staff serving abroad could get quite upset at being cut off from news at home. The fault was immediately rectified.

Fortunately for Mothercat, when Middle East orders were affected by political upheavals, it was able to concentrate on important contracts in Pakistan, which was developing both its electrification supplies and its defence requirements. New Indian contracts also helped take up the slack.

Overseeing foreign contracts was a ruggedly tough frontier life for Motherwell Bridge personnel. Often their work camp sites were situated well out in the desert. With anything from 500 to 1,000 men living in tented accommodation, everything to sustain them, from equipment to food, had to be ferried in. The logistics involved in keeping the sites supplied in temperatures which could range from 120 degrees in the day to freezing point at night were considerable. In fact, they were not much different from planning a military campaign. Most of the local labour used in the Middle East was Palestinian. Many and varied were the stories that filtered back to Motherwell of the strange situations which staff found themselves in. The general manager, and later managing director of Mothercat was Jock

Anderson, nicknamed Tanky, a tough, resourceful boss and a time-served engineer. He was a gruff-spoken Scot, with a hair-trigger temper who had given a lifetime of service to Motherwell Bridge, working his way up the ladder from foreman templatemaker to assistant works manager and then erection manager before being put in charge of the day to day running of Mothercat, and finally being appointed as a director to the main Board in 1966. No respecter of persons, he was a man who spoke his mind and who brooked few excuses over delays. He was highly regarded not only by the Board but by client companies, who recognised him as a man who got things done. They knew that when the hot breath of Jock Anderson was put behind a project, it tended to proceed at a very satisfactory rate, indeed.

In the early days of the formation of Mothercat, however, his individualistic style - and lack of diplomacy - caused more than a little friction with local agents working for CAT. It took some time before the two organisations bedded down into a comfortable working relationship. However, it almost never happened at all.

**DESERT MEETING.** John 'Tanky' Anderson, Alexander Ronald Miller and Forbes D. Masterton.

PIPELAYING IN THE MIDDLE EAST. Chris Fleming-Brown at work in the desert.

# BLACK ARTS OF THE SHOE-SHINE BOYS

AT the time of the creation of the state of Israel in Palestine there was huge anti-European feeling in the Arab world, which felt it had been badly betrayed by the Western powers, and Britain in particular. During this period Ronald Miller visited Cairo, which was being avoided by foreigners because of the dangers.

One American had had his head chopped off and a Frenchman, the coach to the Egyptian Olympic boxing team, had been stabbed to death.

Writing back to head office, Ronald Miller reported: "In Cairo the beggars and street sellers were a real bad lot. You would get a crowd around you in a minute if you dared to argue about a price, or indeed refused to buy their goods ... I refused to have my shoes polished by one man, with the result that another crept up from the back and and covered my shoes with dirt, with the threat that next time they would black-lead my clothes."

The incident didn't cause Ronald Miller to lose his sense of humour, though. He added: "They are good businessmen, for the next street vendor offered to sell me a heavy stick to belt the shoe-cleaners with!"

In 1950, just months before CAT and Motherwell Bridge began trading, the Middle East company was involved in an appalling tragedy. A thief had broken into a store in a residential area where CAT was storing petrol, acetylene and dynamite used for blasting pipe track through the mountains. A fire broke out, and a large crowd gathered to watch - just as the flames ignited the explosives causing a huge blast.

Some 78 local townsfolk died in the explosion and a further 250 were injured. Bustani and his two partners were forced to flee overnight to Cairo as angry Lebanese citizens demanded their arrest. Bustani was almost immediately to voluntarily post £100,000 compensation for the relatives of the dead and injured, irrespective of whether the inquiry held his company to blame for the explosion. But with tensions already high between Lebanon and Syria over trading rights, it was almost a mortal blow to the formation of the joint company, Mothercat. At one point Motherwell Bridge even considered dropping the word "cat" from the new company name. While not directly involved in the tragedy, Motherwell Bridge, because of its association with CAT, for a period found itself on the Government's proscribed list. It was some time before Emile Bustani repaired the rift with the Syrians.

Lack of communications was one of the greatest problems to overcome on foreign contracts. In those days, whenever a company employee was flying home, word would quickly spread round the small foreign community and he would be asked to take sheaves of mail back to the U.K. and post them for a variety of companies in the area. At other times, Motherwell Bridge employees trying to get reports back to head office would have to hang around airports to ask British passengers to take back mail. Embassy staff, shuttling back and forward to the Gulf, were quite used to such requests and cheerfully complied, but the employees did get some old-fashioned looks from less regular travellers. Occasionally the company would 'mislay' staff as happened with Chris Fleming-Brown, grandson of T.R. Miller and a veteran of the later Mothercat days.

The company lost trace of him during what was to be a 32-month stint without home leave. Chris's mother eventually inquired at the Motherwell HQ where her son was because she hadn't heard from him for so long - somewhat to the consternation of the company, which realised it seemed to have misplaced him. Jock Anderson was dispatched to find him. Having finally tracked Chris down to a site in Banias, Syria, the managing director had to hang around for hours at the gate before Chris - who had only been told there was a foreigner wishing to see him - arrived. Jock was less than pleased at having had to cool his heels for so long, but his anger was tempered with relief that the 'lost' staff man was safe and well.

Such logistical problems were as nothing, though, to those encountered in the field. They ranged from the bizarre to the plain dangerous. On one job, erecting prefabricated housing, the local labour force had never encountered opening windows before. They carefully installed them - with all the handles on the outside. For Chris the most frightening incident happened at Abu Dhabi where his two work camps were dependent upon local wells for their water supplies. At one of the wells, Chris laid in a special pipeline to pump water direct to the camp site. However this was not viewed favourably by some of the Arabs in the locality, who regarded it as their water supply. Bedouin tribesmen deliberately dropped items into the well to foul the pump. On one occasion, while trying to retrieve it for repair, a worker was trapped inside the well in a cave-in. All through the day Chris and others desperately tried to free him, but each time they shored the sides of the well, more sand would come tumbling down upon the unfortunate man. Eventually, after despairing of getting him out alive, some eight hours after the original cave-in, they managed to rescue him, whereupon a lone Arab who had been watching the drama all day from a nearby sand dune strolled down and told Chris: "You are a wonderful company".

What he meant, presumably, was that in a land ruled by Arab fatalism and the will of Allah, a local company might not have struggled just so hard in the rescue. In fact, it is one of Chris's proudest accomplishments that in the difficult, and often dangerous, working conditions encountered in remote and inaccessible sites, he never had a single fatality among his work squads - although in the sands of Abu Dhabi it was a close-run thing.

**WATER TOWER.** A 900,000 litre elevated water tank erected by Mothercat at Kufa, Iraq.

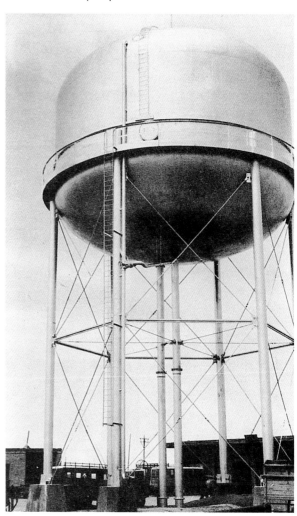

**DAURA REFINERY.** An aerial view of the Iraq Government Refinery at Daura, Baghdad. Most of the tanks were supplied and all were erected by the company. The total number of tanks erected at this refinery was 120.

Not everyone, though, thrived on the challenges of living a spartan existence in the waterless wildernesses of the Gulf. The hours were long and hard, from 4am to 6pm, seven days a week. The climate, too, could unnerve expatriate workers. Although well warned about the conditions, more than one skilled worker stepped off the plane from the UK to be confronted with the baking heat rising off the tarmac - and immediately booked on a flight back to Britain. On one occasion, a complete squad of 17 to 20 men walked off the job and flew back to Britain, prompting a court case over who was responsible for paying the return fares.
(see panel story page 87).

It took a special sort of temperament to handle working abroad in testing terrain and climatic conditions. Although the technology might have changed, the pioneering spirit for developing the Middle East remained as necessary as it once was for the original bridge builders who carried the name of Motherwell Bridge far beyond the shores of Scotland.

**FORBES DAVID MASTERTON.**
Forbes Masterton was a chartered accountant and a key figure in the development of the company. He was seconded to Motherwell Bridge in 1935 from the company's auditors, Brown Fleming & Murray during the illness of the then company secretary Joseph Anderson. When it was established that Mr Anderson would be unfit to return to his duties Forbes was formally appointed company secretary. Everything financial, and a lot more besides, came under his direction and scrutiny and his attention to detail was incredible. He was very much relied upon by both T.R. Miller and A.R. Miller, especially in regard to Mothercat.

It is interesting to note that the company's first auditor was a Mr J. Herbert Wilson who became a partner of Brown Fleming & Murray in 1898, the year of the company's incorporation and that the auditors today are Ernst & Young, the successors to Brown Fleming & Murray after several amalgamations.

MAIN PICTURE: MOTHERCAT AT WORK. A view showing fixed roof storage tanks under construction in the foreground and completed floating roof storage tanks in the background at Fao, Iraq.

Storage Tanks appear to be simple structures, but their site construction requires special skills. The thickness of the steel plates relative to the diameter would be equivalent to a 10″ diameter can made from sheet the thickness of a hair. It is important to maintain the correct diameter of each tier of the tank as it is erected to ensure that a floating roof does not jam or a fixed roof will fit. The welding sequence is also important since contraction occurs at each weld joint resulting in shrinkage of the overall dimensions. Provided contraction is allowed to occur in a controlled manner then good shapes can be achieved, but where this is not allowed to take place, some major distortions can occur.

INSET TOP LEFT: KUWAIT. Welded storage tanks being painted after erection.

INSET CENTRE: Early Horton sphere for Anglo Iranian Oil Co.

INSET BOTTOM LEFT: Aerial view of the Iraq Petroleum Co. Limited tank farm at Banias. 23 storage tanks were supplied from Motherwell and erected by Mothercat.

INSET ABOVE: IRAQ. A welded large floating roof oil storage tank at Fao, Iraq.
In the foreground (from left): George Ibrahim, Mr Nelson, Robert MacLaughlin, William Rae, Elias Issa and Mussif Farah.

CHAPTER 7

Given that the Middle East was such a political hot spot, Mothercat performed very creditably and had a high reputation in the region. It was prone, as ever, to the cyclical nature of the oil industry, which was its principal client, but was instrumental in keeping the Motherwell Bridge profile abroad extremely high. In 1963, though, tragedy struck. Emile Bustani was killed in an air crash, and in the following year the second of the three partners, Abdullah Khoury died suddenly, leaving only Mr Shammas and the two widows to handle business affairs for Bustani's main company, CAT.

It was a tremendous blow. Following the Arab pattern, Mothercat had been built up as a patriarchal system revolving primarily around the larger than life personality of its chief executive and senior partner, Bustani. Almost at long range, Motherwell Bridge found itself having to restructure the company along more traditional British lines of management, which proved both time-consuming and expensive. Despite strenuous efforts by Motherwell Bridge, and heavy investment which rose to more than £1 million, the company was never truly satisfied that it had got the new management structure right.

Mothercat, after a couple of rudderless years, did recover and started returning good profits. But new political stormclouds were gathering in the Middle East. Reluctantly, Motherwell Bridge decided the time had come to sell off its 50 per cent Mothercat holding. Their Middle East partners bought them out in a reciprocal deal which gave Motherwell Bridge Mothercat's overseas tankage division. It immediately was incorporated into Mothercat (Britain) Ltd. which was later renamed Motherwell Bridge Tankage Ltd. The final deal was concluded in January, 1967.

That the directors were right to sell off their Mothercat stake is unquestionable. Within six months Egypt went to war with Israel. Swept into the conflict's vortex were Jordan, Iraq, Syria and Lebanon. The Six Day War may not have lasted long, but it was to turn the Lebanon into a political cockpit for 30 years.

It was a most amicable split. Nevertheless, there was much sadness at the parting of the ways. In, at times, a somewhat grey world of commerce, Mothercat had sparkled with a spirit of adventure, romance and occasionally danger.

It is remembered with great fondness by Motherwell Bridge employees who worked for it, and more than one future executive's leadership qualities were forged on the anvil of its many challenges.

## BOMBAY BEAUTY PARADE

THERE were unexpected perils in doing business abroad for Motherwell Bridge, as Ronald Miller discovered. While in India in 1949, prospecting the possibility of setting up an Indian fabrication shop to benefit from the much lower local steel prices, he quickly discovered that Anglo-Indian partnerships rarely worked very well - because local directors tended to push all their relatives into jobs, irrespective of their abilities. Ronald jokingly mentioned that perhaps the way forward for Motherwell Bridge was for him to marry the daughter of a wealthy, influential family and let her father put up the partnership capital for the Indian venture.

Unfortunately for Ronald, the remark was reported back to a friend of his, the Director of All India Radio, who took it seriously. He got his wife to organise a series of parties for Ronald in Bombay at which girls of every religion, colour and shape were paraded before him. Even though weakened by a bout of malaria, bachelor Ronald, 34, resisted their charms - and scuttled off, with some relief, to Kuwait on business.

On another occasion he had a narrow escape of a different kind. On the spur of the moment he decided to take a week's holiday in India before travelling back to the Middle East. It was a lucky break. The plane he should have travelled on from Karachi to Basra crashed at Bahrain.

86

# A Drop of the Hard Stuff

LONG before Motherwell Bridge became involved with Mothercat the company had a thriving trade in the Middle East. During the war years it wasn't uncommon for Motherwell Bridge men serving in the armed forces to encounter their former colleagues in unexpected places abroad - usually to their mutual advantage.

One such occasion is recalled by 77-year-old former company foreman Bill Law, of New Stevenston, Lanarkshire, who served as a Sergeant in the Royal Engineers during World War II. He says: "In 1945 I was stationed in Haifa looking after anything connected with the British army on the Haifa Docks when quite by chance I met John ('Tanky') Anderson, who was out to inspect work being carried out by the company on a tank farm.

"In charge of the job was Guy Scott and the others included Tom Ross, Dave McCoughtrie and Guy Paterson. There were six Motherwell Bridge men in all. Having to wait for weeks for equipment to arrive, they were there for quite a time. Thanks to my job, I was able to keep them supplied with razor blades, shaving soap and toiletries. In return, I was often invited to their hotel for a meal. My regular service ration of a bottle of whisky always went to Tanky in a straight cash transaction. It cost me 7s 6d (37p) and he always gave me £2 for it."

The Scotch was always a very welcome addition. In Haifa all that was normally available was Egyptian whisky which Bill says "would have blown your head off."

# Test Case over an Air Fare

IN a major labour dispute over the sacking of a welder for bad workmanship, a group of about 20 Motherwell Bridge construction workers in 1949 walked off the job in Kuwait and returned to Britain. It resulted in a test case being raised at the Court of Session two years later over who was responsible for paying the air fares home.

An action against the company was raised in the name of one of the welders, Thomas Duncan. At the time, when sending British workmen abroad, it was company policy for Motherwell Bridge to bank part of the men's wages in a joint savings account in Scotland.

The money deducted - in Duncan's case, £10 per month - acted as a guarantee that workers would stay the course on overseas contracts which tended to last 12 to 18 months, and perform their duties satisfactorily. On the overseas squad's return, the cash - by then a tidy sum - was signed over to them, along with any bonuses due.

In the case of Thomas Duncan, the amount lodged in the bank totalled £124, almost a quarter of his annual salary of £540, when he and the others downed tools and flew back to Britain.

Duncan sued Motherwell Bridge for the cash, claiming the contract he had entered into was invalid under the Truck Acts, which declared such deductions illegal. Motherwell Bridge counter-sued for damages over the disruption of the Kuwait contract and the costs of flying out a replacement worker. It also sought to recover Duncan's return fare, which it had paid.

The Court of Session ruled that deducting cash from Duncan's wages - even with his agreement - was illegal, rendering his contract null and void and also stated Duncan was under no obligation to repay his air fare. On appeal, in a split vote, the Bench ruled Motherwell Bridge was entitled to be recompensed for Duncan's homeward fare. But on the main issue - deducting cash from workmen going abroad - it confirmed the practice to be illegal. The case is still quoted in legal text books.

# JOCK ANDERSON: AN APPRECIATION

THE gentleman watched as the young boy attempted to calm the horse. Mired up to its haunches in boggy ground, it was panicking badly, rolling its eyes and struggling with fear as it sank deeper into the mud. Gently the 14-year-old lad soothed down the animal and eventually managed to bring it safely onto firm ground.

The man approached the teenager as he wiped down the still trembling beast. "Have you got a job, boy?" he asked.

"No sir, but I hope to have one soon."

"Well, you have one now - if you would like to be my coach driver," said the toff, who was Alexander "Paddy" King, managing director and one of the founding members of Motherwell Bridge.

A delighted grin spread over the features of the lad, John Love Anderson. There was nothing he liked better than working with horses. Driving Paddy King from his home in Motherwell to the Bridge Works and out on business calls hardly seemed like work at all.

Thus began a life time's service to Motherwell Bridge by one of its most charismatic employees, Jock Anderson - better known as 'Tanky.' Over the course of 50 years, he was to work in more than 30 countries carrying out and supervising company tankage contracts, principally for the oil industry. For 20 of those years he was based in the Lebanon, looking after Motherwell Bridge's

TANKY in Arab garb.

tankage and construction work in the Middle East.

Barrel-chested, immaculately turned out and always sporting as his personal trademark a bow tie, the stocky figure of Jock Anderson was instantly recognisable wherever he went. In the Middle East, he had a track record that was second to none for bringing in contracts on time, and his knowledge of tankage construction was encyclopaedic. Among the upper echelons of the oil companies his name commanded instant respect. When occasion warranted it, he could lift the phone and speak on first name terms to powerful executives of multi-national companies to sort out problems incapable of being resolved by their on-site management.

He was popular, too, with the Arabs. Used to foreign company men running their overseas operations from a London office, they liked the fact that Anderson preferred to reverse the process. He was a company man based in the Middle East who regularly visited London, rather than the other way round. Very much at ease in their culture, and genuinely enjoying their company, Tanky was a much sought-after guest. Doors within the Arab world were open to him in a way which seldom happened for Westerners. During the days of Mothercat, he even attended an important feast dressed in Arab garb, the first non-Arab ever to attend the event.

His presence at the feast was organised by his great friend, Emile Bustani, the Lebanese pantry boy turned millionaire who founded CAT, the most successful civil engineering and contracting company in the Arab world. Jock was instrumental in bringing together Bustani and Ronald Miller, from which the joint venture, Mothercat, emerged (see main chapter). With very similar swashbuckling personalities, Bustani and Anderson worked well together in Mothercat until Bustani's death in March, 1963, in a freak air accident.

Taking off for Syria in a thunderstorm, Bustani's private plane was forced to turn back to Beirut. While still off the coast, the plane appeared to disintegrate in mid-air, plummetting into the sea. Killed along with Bustani were his Scottish pilot, Captain John Ogilvie, 34, from Kinross, and an English-educated university lecturer, Dr Nimr Touqan. The sudden break-up of the plane while in flight sparked off speculation that a bomb had been planted on board by Bustani's enemies. As a national figure in Lebanese politics he was disliked by opponents because of his pro-Western views. However, there was no strong evidence to support that theory. The most probable cause remains an accident caused by structural failure brought about by extremely turbulent weather conditions. Crashes of light aircraft in the Middle East were a not infrequent occurrence in the 1960s.

Jock Anderson's long spell overseas saw him carry out contracts for Motherwell Bridge with great skill and panache. As already stated, he made many friends in both the ex-patriate and Arab communities. A skilled raconteur with a great sense of humour, he had a fine singing voice and an enormous appetite for life. He could be utterly charming and considerate - a side many Motherwell Bridge personnel did not always see. On-site, he was a driving and energetic boss with at times a quite awesome temper who always bluntly spoke his mind. No-one was ever left in any doubt about Tanky's views.

That said, he was always a boss who gave strong backing to his men if they felt a job was proceeding wrongly. On one

such occasion on a Middle East contract, a Motherwell Bridge welder was being heavily pressured to begin work on an urgent job within an oil refinery. Instinctively, the welder realised there was something wrong, although he couldn't quite pinpoint what it was. Despite heavy pressure from local management, he refused to begin work. Eventually he got through to Tanky and told him he suspected something was amiss, possibly a gas leak. Anderson immediately cabled BP's chief engineer telling him of the welder's concerns. The executive ordered an engineer on-site to carry out a special inspection - and sure enough, a serious gas seepage was discovered. If the welder had proceeded with the job as ordered, a massive explosion might have resulted.

If there was a single quality which defined Tanky it was his boundless energy. He had an immense enthusiasm for work which marked him out right from the start. Apprenticed to Motherwell Bridge by A.C. King at the age of 16, he quickly established himself as the company's best apprentice before going on, after further study, to become Motherwell Bridge's youngest foreman. Rapid promotion saw him also become its youngest assistant works manager, and later its youngest site construction boss before he threw himself, with typical enthusiasm, into his posting to the Middle East.

Getting around the Gulf states, and further afield, in the

1940s and 1950s was not particularly easy. Travel could be long and arduous, but Tanky revelled in his roving role. His remarkable stamina probably stemmed from his youth. A fine athlete, he represented Scotland in the marathon and had a single figure golf handicap. When he moved abroad keeping up with the sport was a lot more difficult, but on his visits back to Scotland, T.R. Miller would make arrangements for him to play one or other of his favourite courses, Royal Troon and Gleneagles.

Jock Anderson's other lifelong passion was horses. He had great success as part-owner of a grey steeplechaser called Clydebridge, which won at Kelso a dozen times and had a race named after it. A regular at Lanark race course when he was back in Scotland, the racing fraternity used to call him the Rajah because of his immaculate dress sense and Middle East tan.

Although not noted for his subtlety, Tanky could be surprisingly devious when it came to cementing good relationships with important clients, something which was not always easy to achieve in the tangled web of Arab politics where Britain, more than once, was cast in the role of villain. Some of his solutions were unorthodox, but they tended to be highly effective. Embarking upon an important joint venture in Egypt with a nationalised engineering company, whose chairman was an Egyptian Colonel, Anderson was worried that because of anti-British feeling the company, for political reasons, was likely to seek out a non-UK partner to replace Motherwell Bridge.

To maintain the special relationship he had established, which continued a long Motherwell Bridge association with the organisation from its pre-nationalisation days, he hit upon an ingenious solution. Under the Nasser Government of the times it was illegal for Egyptians to import cars. But for certain large projects foreign firms were permitted to import a company car as part of plant equipment. On the next plant manifest, Tanky indented for a Mercedes. Its import was approved. The vehicle duly arrived in the next shipment and soon the Colonel was one of an elite band being driven round Cairo in a chauffeur-driven Mercedes. Motherwell Bridge remained the joint venture partner.

With his immense zest for life, an overseas trip with Tanky could be an exhilarating - and exhausting - affair, filled with the unexpected. Former assistant company secretary Iain Macleod recalls one such whirlwind trip, which could have stepped straight from the pages of a film script. Its opening day began in London, with the purchase of Portman Travel, which was to prove the company's most profitable acquisiton (see separate story). The full transaction was completed within that day. Then it was on to Africa, where Tanky spent hours clambering up and down oil storage tanks,

being the only expert trusted by African Petroleum Terminals to advise them on roof replacements.

Day three saw the pair board a flight from Africa to Argentina, then in the throes of political turmoil as unions and students took to the streets in protest marches and a wave of political strikes. It didn't faze Tanky. Within 24 hours he and Macleod were sitting in a Buenos Aires office with an important client discussing requirements for a major contract. Suddenly the door burst open and a Peronist supporter brandishing a sub-machine gun burst into the room. Waving the weapon around alarmingly, he ordered the Argentinians to cease working and go home. The Europeans were ordered to stay in the room.

Anderson, in Macleod's own words, became "frighteningly aggressive," and cursed out the gunman in Arabic, a language he fortunately didn't understand. There was no bloodshed. Despite the threatening encounter, which might have sent many a lesser executive scurrying to the airport for the first flight out, Tanky was there to do business. The following day the meeting was reconvened at a new location, and Motherwell Bridge's business satisfactorily concluded. Nightfall found the pair being feted in a restaurant in La Bocca, the capital's lively Italian quarter. "A Scottish flag was put on our table and a Scottish song sung, in which

Jock joined in," says Macleod. "Before the night was over, Jock was press-ganged into dancing a samba with the staff."

By the weekend, Tanky was back home - and at the races.

Anyone around Tanky for any length of time soon acquired a fund of stories to dine out on. With his commanding presence and boundless energy, he was the sort of person who made things happen. In the Boardroom, his ruggedly independent views made him something of a loose cannon. But in the field there was no-one to touch him. Coupled with great knowledge of his trade was enormous self-confidence. He was a tremendous motivator of people. "Tanky could make you believe you could do anything," says Mothercat veteran Chris Fleming-Brown.

In December, 1969, Jock Anderson retired, although at Ronald Miller's special request he continued to receive full pay until April, 1970, his 65th birthday. He made his home in Cheswick, London, where he lived for 17 years. There, prior to his death in 1987 at the age of 82, Tanky held court, recalling with great gusto the more colourful episodes of a business career that had spanned half a century. He died very much as he had lived: a larger than life character. Decades on, the memories of him remain undimmed wherever Motherwell Bridge veterans congregate to yarn the night away in good fellowship and reminiscence.

# False Dawn of the Nuclear Age

In dramatic silhouette to its surrounds, yet somehow dwarfed by the vast emptiness of the flat and desolate plain of Caithness, Scotland's most northerly mainland territory and one of the most ancient land masses in the world, stands an instantly identifiable man-made landmark, the great metal dome of Dounreay Atomic Research Station. It remains a testament to the early beginnings of the nuclear age in Britain, and a dazzling technological and engineering feat by Motherwell Bridge which time and controversy cannot dim.

As one of Britain's foremost engineering concerns, it was chosen by the United Kingdom Atomic Energy Authority to build and erect the largest metal sphere in Europe to surround the core's fast breeder reactor.

The vast, air-tight metal globe, 135 feet in diameter and weighing 1,500 tons, was nearly three times bigger than any sphere ever built in Britain before and was to be the last line of defence in containing radioactive gases should the many other safety features incorporated in the reactor fail.

Now nearing the end of its life cycle, Dounreay and its distinctive sphere still regularly feature in television newscasts as an acrimonious debate over its future rages. It may continue to have a minor role as a reprocessing plant, taking in other nations' dirty nuclear washing, thereby safeguarding some of the jobs upon which the local community has come to depend over the last 40 years. But many people now argue the risks are too high a price to pay.

**DOUNREAY.** The move by the company into the pressure vessel market in the 1940s gave it the technical confidence to take on the even greater challenge of the infant nuclear era.

Whatever the final outcome of that long-running debate, the truth is that decommissioning nuclear power stations is a lot more difficult than building them.

The central, many would say fatal, flaw which has always dogged the industry remains: no truly safe method has been found for disposing of highly radioactive nuclear waste which can poison earth, sea, fresh water tables and all life's food chains for tens of thousands of years. In terms of energy provision, nuclear power must be considered a blind alley. It is perhaps ironic that if a fraction of the billions of pounds poured into nuclear research had been devoted, on the same Caithness coastline, into self-renewable energy programmes such as wave and wind power, or even geo-thermal energy, much of Scotland might well be today largely self-sufficient in its power requirements. Be that as it may, it does not detract in any way from the considerable accomplishment of Motherwell Bridge in building the Dounreay sphere.

In the mid-fifties the world was in a state of relative innocence about nuclear fission. It was regarded as a 'clean' source of power which would revolutionise energy provision and largely do away with reliance upon the earth's finite supplies of fossilised fuel. The experimental nuclear station at Dounreay was to be the vanguard of that science. Motherwell Bridge, too, got caught up in its false promise.

The magnitude of the task undertaken by Motherwell Bridge at Dounreay was huge. Not only did it chart new frontiers in engineering technology, calling for the most exacting standards of workmanship, particularly in the field of welding, the sphere was also to be built on an extremely tight schedule.

MAIN PICTURE: DOUNREAY SPHERE, LOWER HALF.
The lower half of the sphere had to be erected during July to November 1955 and the upper half during the same period in the next year. The sphere underwent its final four day pressure and vacuum tests during May 1957 and passed with flying colours. At the top can be seen the radial supports which held the structure in shape during the erection process.

INSET: DOUNREAY. The company put heavy resources into this project: here mobile cranes and a derrick crane are in action lowering the various sections into place.
From this photograph one can appreciate the volume of welding required. The centre mast held the radial support arms in position.

MAIN PICTURE: DOUNREAY SPHERE. A view of the containment sphere for the fast "fission breeder" reactor at Dounreay in the final stages of erection. Over 1,500 tons of steel were used and two miles of seams were welded in the construction of the 135 feet diameter sphere.
INSET. Nozzles were fitted to permit the passage of coolant pipework and electric supply cables through the spherical shell.

**MAIN PICTURE: REACTOR CORE.** At this stage of construction the 78 feet diameter reactor vault inside the containment sphere is approaching completion. The reactor vault itself was of concrete construction and this view looks into the reactor chamber. The 'skirts' at the base of the sphere were designed to support the weight of the reactor as well as the sphere itself.

**INSET:** An early stage in the erection of the lower hemisphere.

The A.E.A. wanted it erected in the course of two five-month periods. July to November of 1955 was to be devoted to the erection of the lower half of the sphere; the following year, over the same months, the upper section was to be completed - these, notionally, being the periods when the least severe weather could be expected. Put in charge of the operation were Motherwell Bridge's chief designer, and later general manager, James McLean, with Jack Forrest as erection manager. Site engineer on the project was Gavin (Guy) Scott, who was later to be awarded the MBE for services to the nuclear industry. As befitted such a ground-breaking contract - one, moreover, which Motherwell Bridge thought signposted its future - the company put heavy resources into the project.

The company wasn't quite beginning from a standing start, its close friends Chicago Bridge having built a 225 feet sphere to house the nuclear reactor of one of the USA's first nuclear-powered submarines, the Sea Wolf. Information on much of the technology and metallurgy involved was readily available to them.

Even so, engineering being a highly practical endeavour, Motherwell Bridge had to embark upon many tests of its own to establish the best methods and welding techniques, as well as the type of metal to use for the plates of the sphere. The steel decided upon was Coltuf. While no stronger than ordinary steels, it had the ability to remain unaffected by extremely low temperatures which would turn ordinary steels brittle. In the normal run of things, the sphere was not going to be subjected to such temperatures, but in an emergency, exposure to irradiation from the core would have precisely the same effect as ultra-low temperatures on metal.

Welding, which involved 2 miles of seams across the equivalent of 1.5 acres of metal plating, was also of crucial importance. Designed to have an internal pressure slightly lower than the external atmosphere (to keep gases in), the sphere had to function perfectly. If there was an emergency, its metal surface could be subject to extreme stresses. Any weakness, any flaw such as a small crack in the welding or material would extend itself and open out, resulting in a disastrous failure of the pressure vessel and a complete shutdown of the plant - not just for a few months but for a period of probably 50 years. The entire steelwork within the reactor would be radio-active and unable to be approached for normal repairs. The result would be massive and permanent contamination. All accessible welds, therefore, had to be X-rayed on site.

To meet the time schedule, erection manager Jack Forrest decided to have the sphere's panels prefabricated, two plates at a time, in a special hangar on the site which had previously been used as an aerodrome. Caithness's electricity lines being notoriously subject to power cuts, and probably unequal to the task, the company brought in its own portable generators and transformers to power its welding equipment. It still, however, left a lot of work to be done at the Motherwell end. The bottom section plates of the sphere had to contain apertures for more than 330 cable and pipe entries for connection to the reactor and its controls.

DOUNREAY. Getting close to the final commissioning of the plant.

The nozzles for these were welded at Motherwell, to extremely exacting tolerances, and the plates stress relieved. Indeed, one of the very first challenges Mr Forrest and his squad faced was getting the single largest piece of the bottom hemisphere, which contained an airlock, up to the site from Lanarkshire.

It was so large it had to be sent by sea to the tiny port of Scrabster, near Thurso. There being no cranes in the harbour large enough to unload it, it had to be transported as deck cargo and taken off at low tide, when the deck of the vessel was level with the low-loader brought up to take it on the last stage of the journey. Skids were used to lever it onto dry land. The operation went off without a hitch, much to the relief of all concerned.

## A RIVAL'S SALUTE

WHESSOE LIMITED, of Darlington, had long been one of Motherwell Bridge's principal rivals in England - despite the two companies being joint licencees of Chicago Bridge for floating roof tanks. However, there was a great deal of mutual respect between the organisations. On the death of T.R. Miller, Whessoe posted the news on its company bulletin board, sent representatives to his funeral and later ran a tribute to his life and times in the company magazine.

T.R. was regarded as one of the industry's pioneer figures and was as well known to Whessoe foremen and others whom he often met at remote sites around the world, as he was to his own company staff.

The greatest challenge, however, was not the technology; it was the elements. Caithness is one of the most exposed areas of Scotland, subject to a truly remarkable clash of weather systems coming in off the sea and encountering the first major land mass for hundreds of miles. Its flat plains are swept by constant winds, which regularly gust beyond 100 miles an hour. As Jack Forrest was to remark feelingly:

"The construction team engaged on the Dounreay sphere had more than their fair share of occupational difficulties to overcome. The sight of a sunlit sphere silhouetted against a calm, blue sea was one which seemed to be reserved for visiting dignitaries. To the average person engaged in Dounreay the scene usually presented was a bleak, overcast sky, a howling wind and great white waves dashing themselves against the cliffs. There were few days when the wind wasn't blowing at more than 40 miles an hour. Work was carried on under all but the very worst conditions. If it hadn't, the sphere would still be a pile of plates lying around waiting for a calm day."

Not for nothing had wartime soldiers stationed a few miles away across the Pentland Firth on the Island of Hoy memorised a poem whose every verse finished, "In bloody Orkney." Caithness may have been on the mainland, but, if anything, it was subject to even more gales than that windswept archipelago.

Nevertheless, the Motherwell Bridge outside squad conquered the elements sufficiently to bring in the job on time, which was quite a feat, considering that the welding had to be done by hand, 75 per cent of it working from stagings high up on the sphere. At other times, the men found themselves in enclosed spaces inside it, having to weld over zinc. To prevent nausea and sickness from the zinc fumes, they were required to drink a pint of milk a day.

On 22nd May, 1957, the sphere underwent its final pressure and vacuum tests, a process which took four days. It passed with flying colours, and was formally handed over to the nuclear energy authorities.
The whole of Motherwell Bridge was enthused by the achievement. A special workers' bus trip to Caithness to see it was organised - a round trip of some 700 miles - and specially designed table lighters, mini replicas of the Dounreay sphere, were issued by the company to works staff as a permanent memento of the achievement.

However, there was to be little respite for site construction manager Jack Forrest. He was moving on to a new site management job for the company, this time in Ayrshire. Motherwell Bridge, having successfully cut its teeth on Dounreay, was readying itself to fully embrace the new nuclear age. Having joined a consortium involving the General Electric Company, Simon-Carves Ltd. and John Mowlem and Co. Ltd., the company was to help build for the South of Scotland Electricity Board the then biggest nuclear power station in the world. Its name - Hunterston.

The Lanarkshire company's slice of the £40 million contract was costed at £8.5 million. The new task being embarked upon was the most ambitious ever undertaken in company history. But it was to be a very different proposition from Dounreay. The huge development on the Ayrshire coast came close to being the undoing of Motherwell Bridge as it swallowed up every resource that management executives could fling at it - and then demanded more. The Hunterston project, in fact, was the decisive factor in launching Motherwell Bridge in an entirely different direction on its completion, less out of choice than out of necessity. Because of Hunterston, the company was forced to radically rethink and alter its trading profile.

The date of the announcement that the Hunterston contract had been awarded to the group, in competition against three other UK consortia, perhaps held a clue as to what lay in store. It was Thursday, 13th December, 1956, a less than propitious omen. By Christmas of that year, Motherwell Bridge had negotiated the largest overdraft in its history, £1 million, so that it could "tool up" for the job ahead. It was to be only the first of huge demands to be made upon the company, financially and technically. The first thing that has to be said about Hunterston is that everything about it was on the grand scale - from manpower (which at its peak involved thousands of people, UK-wide) to volume of materials and site preparation. Its steelwork requirements, alone, at 15,000 tons, were eight times that of Dounreay.
In terms of heavy engineering, just about everything that Motherwell Bridge was required to produce for Hunterston broke all existing norms. It was an exercise in constant trail-blazing.

HUNTERSTON. The top section of the first reactor pressure vessel being lifted into position. The pilot holes for control-rod standpipes, and the nozzles for the eight gas ducts, can be clearly seen.

HUNTERSTON. The 350-ton reactor support grid being lowered into the biological shield.

Every step of the way was paved with new records; it must have seemed to an at times embattled workforce as if every component involved was the biggest, the heaviest, the thickest, the tallest in the world, all to be produced to the most exacting of tolerances. And so was the machinery being used to fashion and construct it.

There was another factor, also. Being the largest civilian nuclear project of its kind on earth, Motherwell Bridge found its activities being conducted in the full glare of media publicity. The newspapers of the day, not to mention specialist publications, were keenly interested. It fairly quickly became apparent that the 300 megawatt Hunterston power station, destined to fulfil one-fifth of the South of Scotland's electricity needs, was going to be an

engineering contract on which reputations would be made, and broken.

It all started out promisingly enough. On New Year's Day, 1958, the first 20 Motherwell Bridge men moved on site to start ground preparations - a workforce which within 16 months was to build up steadily to 480 and a site staff of around 100. In the later stages in 1960-61 the site workforce reached almost 1,000 men.

The planning which had gone into Motherwell Bridge's part of the project was meticulous. The company was to build 16 massive heat exchangers and the two 70 feet diameter spheres to house the two gas-cooled reactors in Hunterston's twin towers, which between them would contain a total of 500 tons of uranium. The cores themselves were to be protected by 10 feet thick concrete biological shields, but there was still a requirement to have the pressure vessels constructed out of extremely thick metal. The spheres were to be made out of hot-pressed 3-inch thick Coltuf steel plates. To bend the plates, Motherwell Bridge had spent more than a year designing and building at a cost of £50,000 its own 2,000-ton press. Designed by the company's chief designer, James McLean, the press, itself, was one of the largest made anywhere in the world at that time.

Handling the weight involved when manoeuvring the plates into position on-site was another record-breaking design task for the company. It had to have constructed the world's largest Goliath crane, a 200 feet high monster capable of lifting 300 tons (it was actually tested to lifts of 350 tons). Capable of moving one-fifth of a mile across the site, the crane worked first on one tower, then the second. Just creating and erecting it, alone, was a major engineering feat. Motherwell Bridge also had to build what was, in essence, a complete and self-sufficient fabrication shop on the site. The £1 million complex, equipped with two 40-ton electric travelling cranes, contained welding booms, turntables, roller bed bogies, a horizontal drilling machine, a stress relieving furnace, surface tables and many other pieces of equipment. Rail lines were laid in, and on the site there was also a specialised welding school (to train welders up to A1 skills). Also on site were the myriad state of the art testing machines required to check every inch of every weld - again, as in Dounreay, one of the key features of the construction work.

Back at head office, the company had not been idle, either. A new £250,000 office block, needed principally to house additional drawing office, design and technical staff, was commissioned and built - a now familiar pattern. Motherwell Bridge was discovering that to service the Hunterston contract it was constantly having to bring on board new experts. New internal departments were having to be set up embracing metallurgy, research and design. Drawing office and technical staff increased. On the shop floor, as the contract progressed, greater and greater numbers of workers were involved in Hunterston steelwork, creating bottlenecks on other jobs. A lot of it was slow work because of its exactitude. It also involved many odd measurements. One of the most finicky tasks concerned

the lower plates of the spheres. As for the Dounreay sphere, the Motherwell shop welded on the many nozzles required for cable and pipe work. But this time there was an added layer of complexity. The company also had to construct, for insertion into the biological shield of the reactor, a 350-ton grid to support the reactor core. Its holes had to be aligned absolutely exactly. The slightest miscalculation would run the risk of leaving fuel rods unable to be serviced.

Hunterston, like some insatiable, many-tentacled beast, in virtually every department was beginning to dominate executives' time and energy. What it all added up to was the tail was beginning to wag the dog.

Ronald Miller, now entering his fifth year as joint managing director, was to confess in 1958: "In the field of nuclear work, the call for standards of workmanship and research technique, taken together, are beyond anything we have previously experienced ..." It was a clear admission that Motherwell Bridge, for all its well deserved reputation for engineering excellence, was perilously close to being out of its depth. It was attempting, in an accelerated learning curve, to graft onto its business a complex and extremely demanding new science which other larger engineering concerns had taken years to assimilate. That position was to be compounded by serious delays on-site through wildcat strikes and lengthy on-site union meetings.

# ISLE OF GRAIN SUCCESS

NOT all of Motherwell Bridge's energies were devoted to Hunterston. In the 1950s it successfully completed one of the largest contracts in Britain for the oil industry at Isle of Grain refinery. It erected a total of 115 crude oil tanks and 13 Hortonspheres. The steelwork involved, more than 25,000 tons, was greater than Hunterston.

The huge contract, despite adverse weather conditions involving rain, frost, snow and fog, took just 30 months to complete by an outside squad numbering, at its peak, 470 men. To cut down construction time on the massive development - phase two of the refinery - work was carried out simultaneously on as many as 21 sites at a time, involving Motherwell Bridge in a huge logistical exercise distributing steel and supplies. Despite the difficulties, the squad averaged more than 800 tons a month.

MAIN PICTURE: HUNTERSTON. An aerial view of the Hunterston Magnox Nuclear Generating Station with the A and B reactor buildings standing out from the Ayrshire countryside. The Clyde estuary appears at the top left.

INSET: STEAM-RAISING UNITS. One of the 16 steam-raising units being positioned by the 300-ton Goliath portal crane prior to being raised into a vertical position on its support. Another unit can be seen in position in the background. These units were double pressure, water tube boilers with assisted circulation. Each unit had a total gas volume of 18,000 cubic feet, with an inlet gas temperature of 396°C and an outlet gas temperature of 200°C. The reactor was gas cooled using carbon dioxide ($CO_2$) and the hot $CO_2$ from the reactor was pumped through the SRUs and returned to the reactor at the lower temperature in a continuous circulating process.

INSET: SRU LIFT. A steam-raising unit being lifted from the on-site workshop rail bogie. The pressure shell is 19 feet 6 inches in diameter and is 73 feet in length and weighs 210 tons. In this photograph the large number of tubes in the steam-raising unit tube bank can readily be seen.

The on-site disputes brought about a constant erosion of time schedules and huge dislocation of the work flow. The logistics of handling any major construction contract is rather like conducting a large orchestra: each section has to come in precisely on the command of the conductor's baton or chaos results. The various trades find themselves hampered by the log-jam of tasks which have to be carried out before they are able to get on with their own work. In the normal way of things, the 'black art' of keeping a site contract running smoothly can be disrupted by many external factors often outwith a company's control, such as weather conditions, breakdown of machinery or delays from outside suppliers. When numerous wildcat strikes are thrown into the equation the logistics become downright impossible.

The extent of the dislocation of work at Hunterston can be imagined by statistics compiled by Motherwell Bridge for part of the contract. In a 19-month period from February, 1958, to September, 1959, there were a total of 32 strikes, plus, in a six-month period in 1959, no less than 60 on-site union meetings, which often went on for hours. Over a seven-month period in 1958-59 Ronald Miller calculated that unofficial stoppages and meetings caused an unprecedented loss of 55,000 man hours - almost 14 per cent of the total hours which should have been worked. Desperately trying to keep the contract moving, site management found itself involved in 471 meetings with union shop stewards - of which 174 concerned demands for extra money, and 13 concerned bans on overtime.

Even given the labour militancy of the times, and the demarcation disputes between trades which bedevilled heavy industry and manufacturing, it was to lead site erection manager Jack Forrest, looking back on those days, to seriously wonder whether the contract was being deliberately sabotaged by professional agitators. "There certainly were an enormous number of disputes. We seemed to have unofficial stoppages every two or three days," he says.

Striking at the very core of the project were serious problems over the welding. Notwithstanding the fact that Motherwell Bridge had scoured Britain for the best welders around (and were paying enhanced wages nearly double the average welding rates), the failure rate was running at 40 per cent. The expense and delay caused by

STRESS RELIEVING. The operator is checking the electrical elements that have been installed prior to stress relieving of the reactor at Hunterston.

cutting out welds which were not up to the exceptionally high standard required were considerable.

That situation was not helped, either, by the fact that the caulkers and welders were the most militant workers on site. Their demands accounted for almost half of the 471 management-union meetings.

Labour relations were not the only problem. Specifications were being changed almost on a daily basis; hardly had a set of schematics arrived on site than another for the same job would come winging on its way from the drawing office, with numerous differences. Under the strain of constant changes and slipping deadlines, the back-biting on site continued. Nor was it happening in a vacuum. Motherwell Bridge, during the Hunterston period, was hit by two other thunderbolts of misfortune which greatly affected morale. In the Autumn of 1957 it found itself embroiled in a nightmarish dispute over the ordering of steel principally for oil tankage work. Because of the UK steel quotas system designed to regulate supply shortages, it was the custom of firms to book steel considerably in advance of orders from a variety of sources. The company discovered that it appeared to have been committed to the purchase of 9,000 tons of continental steel, valued at nearly £1 million, for which

AN SRU BEING LIFTED FROM THE WORKSHOP.

A completed steam-raising unit being lifted from its specially constructed workshop bogies by the 300-ton Goliath crane outside the Hunterston workshop prior to positioning on its support adjacent to the reactor. Earlier the unit would have undergone a stress relieving process by being heated to a temperature of 600-650°C and held at this level for four hours. To do this the units were insulated and hot gas blown through the units from an external combustion chamber. The system supporting the units during this process had to be capable of allowing for lengthwise expansion without causing distress to the vessel. Following stress relief the units were hydro-tested.

it had no orders - and little prospect of laying off in other directions. It was eventually to resolve the situation, incurring an out of court settlement of a fraction of that figure. But it was a protracted affair, taking three years to settle, and its financial uncertainties long overshadowed its other operations.

The following year in September, 1958, T.R. Miller, the man who was the very embodiment of Motherwell Bridge, died suddenly after a short illness, at the age of 78 years. If, in the last couple of years of his life, more of his duties had been shouldered by his son, he remained - to the workforce - a most potent talisman. As long as T.R. was around, they felt, the company's future was assured, and now he was no longer with them at one of the most testing periods in the company's history. It was a deeply despondent time for the company and its employees. Rumours were rife that Ronald Miller was going to sell out to GEC and retire to

the Middle East - scuttlebutt which the new man at the helm quickly and publicly rebutted.

He also speedily appointed two new directors. Mr A.L.G. (later Sir Arnold) Lindley, a managing director of GEC, Motherwell Bridge's main Hunterston partner, was brought onto the board to consolidate the company's nuclear work, and company secretary Forbes Masterton was elevated to the Board to "eliminate any wasteful methods" of production, a task for which he was eminently suited.

For Ronald Miller, at 43 years of age assuming the full mantle of managing director and chairman, it was a baptism of fire. He took complete control of the company at a time when it was perilously close to being overwhelmed by the Hunterston contract; elsewhere in its traditional spheres of activity, orders were not keeping pace with steel deliveries and conditions within the oil industry looked deeply unpromising for the

MAIN PICTURE: 2,000-TON PRESS. To preform the plates prior to manufacture for the Hunterston project the company had spent a year designing a new 2,000-ton press. This press in 1956 was one of the largest in the world and cost the company some £50,000. It was installed by John Young & Co., now a Motherwell Bridge subsidiary.

FAR RIGHT: OFFICE WATER TOWER. This water tower was built in front of the old offices and beside the new office block during 1959 and was based on a similar Chicago Bridge water tower. It was more of a company product symbol than a necessity although it did supply a 'head' of water for the works and offices.

BELOW: FOOTBALL TEAM. The Motherwell Bridge football team and its committee in Girvan on their 1956 annual outing.

immediate future. The only gleam of optimism, in fact, came from Mothercat, which after a couple of indifferent years of trading, was returning record profits. But it was Hunterston which principally pre-occupied the company. The contract continued to be dogged by labour troubles.

Crisis point over Hunterston was reached in March, 1959, when Ronald Miller summoned a mass meeting of workers at Hunterston to inform them that unless progress could be greatly improved Motherwell Bridge would withdraw from the contract. It was no idle threat, and would have affected some 200 sub-contractors across Scotland. But having reviewed the operation, now a full year behind schedule, the new boss had reached the conclusion that if the present slow rate of progress continued the losses incurred by the end of the contract would be too great for the company to sustain. There was a very real danger of Hunterston putting the

company out of business. There was a concerted effort to improve labour relations. Introduced on the site was a Joint Production and Advisory Committee, similar to the one which had so successfully defused potential labour-management flashpoints at Motherwell for several years. The company also paid bonuses ranging from £5 to £20 for good suggestions from the workforce on ways to improve productivity and working practices. It also made major purchases of yet more plant.

In a bid to get things moving, the company was prepared to bring on site more equipment, for which it would have no other use than at Hunterston. For a time working relationships improved, but the uneasy truce finally disintegrated in the autumn of 1959. August and September were wicked months for labour troubles and lost man-hours. Indeed, in September, work on-site was brought almost to a complete standstill by four separate strikes. Once again, the company attempted to negotiate on the claims. But while in the middle of negotiations with union bosses, some of the men who had returned to work pending discussions went out on strike again. For Ronald Miller, it was the last straw.

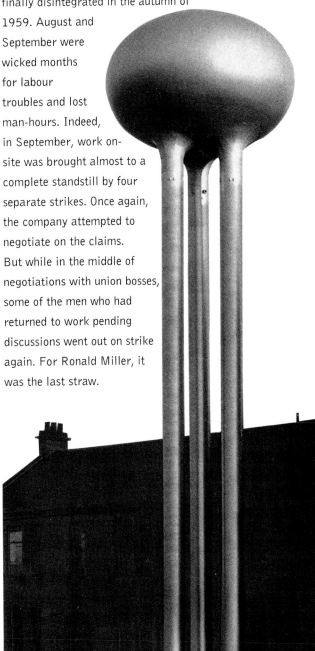

# CHAPTER 8

On September 25 the company suspended all operations on the site, stating work would not resume at Hunterston until more satisfactory conditions pertained. Progress on the contract did not resume until January, 1960. The three-month 'cooling off' period seemed to have been a salutary lesson to everyone and work began to proceed at a much more satisfactory pace.

In an attempt to kill several birds with one stone, the managing director decided upon a management team shake-up. Site construction manager Jack Forrest was brought back to head office to streamline operations of plant and machinery, sadly out of kilter because everyone's attention seemed to be focused upon Hunterston. Brought to Hunterston as project manager in June, 1960, was chartered engineer John Crawford, an energetic young 30-year-old New Zealander who a few years earlier had come back to see the mother country, working his passage to England on board a merchant ship as a junior engineer. He had joined Mobil Oil, then moved to Motherwell Bridge. With his broad engineering knowledge, his task at Hunterston was to improve welding performance and productivity.

Abroad, interest in Hunterston remained undiminished. In May of that year more than 200 delegates attending a symposium at the Royal College of Science and Technology, Glasgow, on nuclear reactor containment buildings and pressure vessels, visited both the Hunterston site and the Motherwell works in what was the largest company visit ever organised. Representatives numbered many foreign experts from Italy, Spain, Holland, Switzerland, Portugal, France, Sweden, Austria, Yugoslavia, Poland, Denmark, Norway, Belgium, Germany and the USA. Hunterston, despite its problems, was still regarded as a world landmark in nuclear technology, but for Motherwell Bridge and the consortium the prestige which came their way could not conceal the fact that on Hunterston there were no victories to be won - only defeats to be avoided.

True to form, as it entered its final stages it involved the company in yet another record-breaking achievement in technology. The two reactor vessels had to be individually stress relieved in what were the biggest single heat treatments of complete structures ever undertaken in the world.

Stress relief of metal is carried out on structures which have been welded together from metal plates.

GOLIATH CRANE. Goliath crane erecting itself. The centre bridge was raised using the outer supporting legs and lifting mechanism.

The tremendous heat generated by the welding process causes localised expansion and contraction which is resisted by the cooler surrounding metal, 'locking in' stress to the platework around each weld. This internal stress within the metal is relieved by heating the structure until it is red hot, making the steel sufficiently plastic for the stresses to relax evenly and gradually into the next plate and across the entire surface. In the heat process it is extremely important that the whole structure is raised to a uniform temperature and is also allowed to cool evenly.

At Hunterston, because of many additional steel internal units within the two spheres, calculating the amount of heat required to bring them to a uniform temperature of

108

600 degrees C. was an exceptionally complex task - as was the actual heating process, itself. A special electric heating system had to be created in the form of 100 feet heating strips supported by wire links and insulators. Each heating unit had to be exactly positioned within the sphere to ensure even increases in temperature across the whole surface. Motherwell Bridge's John Crawford tackled the sphere for Hunterston's 'A' reactor first. Some 400 special thermal sensors were placed throughout the shell of the pressure vessel to check temperatures, and the 70 feet sphere was also thoroughly lagged externally to prevent major heat loss. The command console in the control room, which was situated within the biological shield, also had to be specially designed, as had many of the instruments recording the stress relief operations. The procedure was carried out successfully, as was the 10-day cooling period, then later repeated on the second reactor vessel.

Pressure testing, which also included some of the ducting, was another massive operation. It took place in mid-winter. Being temperature sensitive, screens were erected to cut down on wind chill, but the day before the test began, most of them were destroyed in a small fire. Again, thermal links were used to raise the temperature as required. The biggest challenge, though, was keeping the relays of compressors running continuously for days on end as something like 200 inspectors swarmed over the construction, checking on apertures and seals. The operation took three days to complete, working round the clock. The inspectors used to grab a few hours' sleep, bedding down in the canteen which had been turned into a make-shift dormitory. Off the coast, patrol boats were on constant vigil, warning off any small craft

GOLIATH. A 300-ton Goliath portal crane 203 feet high, span 203 feet, and weighing some 1,500 tons was constructed for the Hunterston project. The crane had to be capable of moving 350 yards across the site. The crane was designed by the French company Applevage and built by Motherwell Bridge. It was intended to build a second crane and steel was purchased for this but no further action was taken. Some of the steelwork was used in combining the existing buildings acquired from Scottish Oils at Uphall with the re-located ex-Hunterston workshop to make the new heat exchanger facility.

from coming too close to the power station during the tests. If anything had gone wrong, it could have resulted in a massive (non-nuclear) explosion. However, once again the structures reached approved standards.

Even the longest night passes.

The Hunterston contract which had started out with such high hopes in 1956 limped to its conclusion in the Spring of 1963. The last heavy lift on the contract took place almost a year earlier on 10th May, 1962, when the final steam-raising unit weighing 230 tons was raised into position, watched by industrial correspondents from the UK press, and BBC and STV camera crews. The completion of Hunterston was not quite the last chapter for Motherwell Bridge.
The contract had proved so complex, and the delays and alterations to specifications so considerable, that it took a couple of years for the consortium to unravel the various strands and agree upon final payments from GEC, which as main contractor handled negotiations with the SSEB.

Long before that happened, though, Motherwell Bridge had come to terms with the practicalities of its wholehearted venture into the nuclear age. From early 1961 and even before, it had known it had to find new, and different, work to 'mop up' its large complement of additional resources spawned by Hunterston: it had a sizeable amount of plant lying around, surplus to its requirements for its normal operations; it had new departments heavily staffed by research and technology experts for whom it would have to find new work (over the Hunterston contract, white collar staffing in Motherwell Bridge throughout Britain jumped four-fold to 400); and it had been concentrating so fiercely on overcoming the problems of Hunterston that 'bread and butter' work had very often gone by the board. It was not a healthy situation. The time had come for a rapid and far-reaching re-assessment of the company's strengths and a re-evaluation of where it was going.

# SELLAFIELD PUZZLER SOLVED

WHEN one of Sellafield's air-cooled graphite reactors caught fire in 1957, contaminating part of a 390 feet high vent stack, it was to Motherwell Bridge that it turned for help. A 60 feet upper section of the reinforced high concrete and steel chimney required to be removed. First, though, it had to be left alone for a number of years to allow radioactive decay to reach a level where dismantling could be safely undertaken. Even so, it was a tricky operation.

Workmen taking down the affected section still had to be protected from radiation. Motherwell Bridge solved the safety problem by designing and erecting a special dismantling system known as the Chimney Access Tower (CAT) which kept the men radiologically shielded while they removed the damaged section. The contract was successfully completed within budget and well within safety norms.

SELLAFIELD. A 390 feet high vent stack being dismantled at Sellafield utilising the latest technology by Motherwell Bridge Nuclear, the specialist decommissioning operation within the group.

# IAN ST. JOHN'S HIGH FLYING DAYS

ONE of Motherwell Bridge's most famous ex-employees is former top footballer and Scotland internationalist Ian St. John, the well-known TV sports commentator. Football-mad Ian left Colvilles, which didn't have a works team, to join Motherwell Bridge as an apprentice plater. It was not exactly coincidence that Motherwell Bridge at the time had a highly successful works side, then coached by Archie Patrick, a shrewd judge of soccer talent who often scouted for the major clubs. Very quickly the new signing became Motherwell Bridge's star player, with coach Archie predicting: "That lad's going to be a top player. He's got it all."

A popular figure around the work, Ian, even then, had a ready tongue in his head, and was never stuck for an answer if he was pulled up by a gaffer, asking what he was doing. However, one day he and a couple of mates met their come-uppance when they were suspected of sneaking off to a hut for a card session. A yard craneman hoisted it a good 15 feet in the air, and left the trio dangling until he reckoned they had learned their lesson.

Ian went on to join Motherwell FC, where he became their top goal scorer. And the rest, as they say, is history.

IAN ST JOHN. Ex-employee Ian St. John doing what he was so good at doing – scoring goals. In this shot it was another in the net for Motherwell Football Club.

To Ronald Miller the answer seemed clear: diversification. Never again was Motherwell Bridge going to be caught with most of its financial eggs in one basket.

The final epitaph on nuclear work, though, could have been said to have been pronounced by Ronald Miller in 1961 when, with commendable frankness, he reviewed company operations and stated publicly: "In Hunterston we were involved in the largest and most difficult financial project in the company's history. I believe every company that has tackled a nuclear power station in Britain has lost money, except perhaps the civil engineering companies. Although every other company started with existing and usually large technical staffs, we started virtually from scratch and were forced to use crash methods to catch up. Unfortunately those methods, although necessary, tended to divert our efforts from other important company activities.

It also left some doubts in our minds upon the solidity of the foundations upon which rested this vastly larger and rapidly created organisation."

For Motherwell Bridge, the nuclear age was over. It was not to return to it, other than in minimal form, for decades. With a certain degree of irony, it became involved in site restoration of nuclear power stations being decommissioned.

Hunterston was far from being all bad news. It had brought work into the company, maintaining full employment, much of it in a period of slack trading which Ronald Miller described as the worst in 30 years. But the bigger nuclear generating stations already on the drawing boards in Britain and elsewhere appeared to be looking to concrete as a cheaper option to steelwork. For its future prosperity, Motherwell Bridge was going to have to look elsewhere.

# TAKE A LETTER, MISS GOULD

Women continuing to work after marriage was frowned upon by bosses? Here is an agreement typist Sarah Gould, of the London office, had to sign in May, 1938, at the insistence of T.R. Miller.

I, Miss Sarah Gould, do hereby agree to conform with the essential rules and regulations set out below -

1. In the event of my desiring to leave I must give three Calendar Months' notice, whereas the Company need only give me the usual notice.
2. I also agree to give loyal service and every satisfaction both in my work and the hours delegated to me. So that should it be necessary to work elastic hours I will make no demur or appear impatient.
3. My domestic affairs shall in no way interfere with my job, otherwise there is no alternative to dismissal.
4. Regarding my personal appearance, I undertake to be as well turned out in the future as in the past, so that my employer need have no cause to reprimand me.

# THE DRINKER'S DITTY

The horse and cow live 30 years
And nothing know of wines or beers;
The goat and sheep at 20 die
And never taste of Scotch or Rye;
The cow drinks water by the ton
And at 18 its life is done;
The dog at 15 cashes in
Without the aid of Rum or Gin;
The cat in milk and water soaks
And then at 12 short years it croaks;
The modest, sober, bone dry hen
Lays eggs for years and dies at 10;
All animals are strictly dry
They sinless live- and sinless die;
But sinful, wineful, rum-soaked men
Live on for three score years and ten
And some of us - the mighty few
Stay pickled till we're 92.

*Contribution to a 1950s works magazine*

# THE ESTIMATOR'S NIGHTMARE

ORDERING steel in the 1950s was a highly complex business. In the post-war years there were huge backlogs of steel orders for reconstruction work.

The Government imposed strict quotas. Anything regarded as non-essential work went to the end of the queue. Often, because of shortages, the steel mills themselves imposed their own quotas on top of the Government quotas. It was important, therefore, for Motherwell Bridge to have extremely good business contacts within the steel industry.

With its close and historic links to Colvilles, Motherwell Bridge was well served. At Board level, directors negotiated a regular weekly tonnage allocation of steel from Colvilles and its various steelworks. It was a gentleman's agreement which allowed Motherwell Bridge at times to cancel allocations without fear of penalty because there were usually plenty of takers for any surplus not taken up.

Under the system, Motherwell Bridge buying and estimating departments then followed up, placing the detailed orders and specifications with Colvilles' various works. A strict ratio had to be maintained between light and heavy plates ordered. If Motherwell Bridge deviated from it, the company lost out on maximum deliveries, which could cause shortages further down the line which were impossible to make good. Thus estimators had to 'marry up' steel availability with customers' requirements so that the two matched.

As if that wasn't complicated enough, another major factor came into play. It was the practice of oil companies to reserve annual tonnages of steel from Motherwell Bridge up to two years ahead, having roughly calculated likely needs for tankage and other work. They then would draw on that tonnage as required when the finalised contracts were prepared and the precise specifications known.

Contractors like Motherwell Bridge were paid the going rate per ton at the time of usage.

As a wide-spread industry practice to minimise delays in obtaining material, it operated fairly satisfactorily. Not unnaturally, it involved a high degree of goodwill and trust between companies and most firms like Motherwell Bridge normally only entered into such agreements with long-established customers.

Its drawback was that huge sums of money and material were being pledged between the various parties on little more than letters of intent - the validity of which had never been tested in contract law. Twice in the 1950s the company found itself on the wrong side of 'an agreement to enter into an agreement' in which the other party construed letters of intent to be firm orders.

In 1957, Motherwell Bridge found itself faced with a 'black hole' in its financial commitments. It discovered one of its estimators appeared to have committed the company to the purchase of 9,000 tons of high-priced continental steel through steel brokers P. McCallum, whom it had recently started using for foreign supplies to fulfil urgent orders for clients.

The dispute centred over an exchange of letters between the two parties, and hinged on usage of English language. Motherwell Bridge maintained that throughout the correspondence it had merely 'reserved' stocks for 1959, as was common practice, without full commitment to buy because the customers' specifications were still undecided. P. McCallum interpreted the word 'reserve' as a 'firm booking', then followed up with another letter confirming that it 'had sold' to Motherwell Bridge 9,000 tons of steel.

The matter only came to light when the hapless Motherwell Bridge estimator involved in writing the letter of intent attempted to resign. Motherwell Bridge took Counsel's opinion, intending to dispute any liability through the courts. However, the company was advised that it was by no means certain they would win the case. Under contract law, the Scottish courts had already laid down a precedent which stated:
"The judicial task is not to discover the actual intention of each party; it is to decide what each was reasonably entitled to conclude from the attitude of the other."

At first the company's liabilities looked like being of the order of £750,000 for steel which wasn't due to be used until 1959. However, by dint of negotiation with Esso, for whom the bulk of material had been reserved, the steel companies involved and with P. McCallum, a process which took three years, the company settled the matter out of court for a fraction of that sum.

Another 'advance reservation' landed Motherwell Bridge in litigation. In 1956 the same estimator placed reservations totalling 3,000 tons with a sub-contractor, R. and J. Dempster, for part of its steel quotas for 1958, 1959 and 1960, "prices to be settled at a later and appropriate date."

Motherwell Bridge needed the steel because its own quota was not going to be sufficient to meet an expected upsurge in tankage contracts. However, the expected orders did not materialise and the company did not take up the reservations. R & J. Dempster sued for breach of contract. The test case was heard at the Court of Session in 1964 before Lord Wheatley who in a lengthy judgment ruled that the 'reservation' letters were a valid and binding commercial contract, and that price was not an essential element since the contract concluded was not a contract of sale. R & J Dempster was awarded damages of £50,000.

Motherwell Bridge lodged an appeal. It was heard before Lord Clyde, the Lord President, sitting with Lords Carmont and Guthrie. Lord Clyde, in a 15-page judgment, with their Lordships concurring, upheld the lower court decision. For Motherwell Bridge the watershed case was a costly end to a widespread industry practice which was far more risky than most companies had previously supposed.

# BULL'S EYE TACTICS

GUY SCOTT. Gavin (Guy) S. Scott at an Investiture at Buckingham Palace on 13th March 1962 to receive the MBE, accompanied by his wife and daughter. Guy received an MBE for services to industry in the construction of Dounreay.

ONE of the great characters of Motherwell Bridge was works manager Guy Scott. Nicknamed The Bull, he was not noted for his tact and diplomacy. Nevertheless, when occasion demanded, he could finesse his way out of awkward situations. As site manager at Dounreay he came up against an unexpected situation which had the potential of gravely embarrassing the company - and making headline news.

It was reported to him that one of the radioactive isotopes wasn't in its special lead chamber, known as a 'bomb.' Used for radiography tests on welds, it had been lost on site. Scott's big problem was clearing the area to look for it without alerting anyone as to what was going on. He solved it by sacking a shop steward on the spot over a minor labour dispute. An angry outside squad walked off the job in protest. While the men were off-site Scott had it checked over, using Atomic Energy Authority geiger counters. The missing isotope was quickly located and returned to its container. Immediately Scott defused the strike by reinstating the dismissed man, saying he had acted too hastily.

On another occasion, though, The Bull was bested by an apprentice. At Motherwell Bridge, just before the siren went to signal the end of the shift, it was The Bull's practice to stand at the gates and 'quarter' (dock time sheets by 15 minutes) anyone he suspected of idling away the last few minutes, waiting for the whistle to go.

On the shop floor was an apprentice who played in a local band. A talented cornet player, he was able to get a tune out of virtually anything. A few minutes before the shift's end, using his horn-playing skills, he picked up a length of pipe and managed to produce from it a loud note which sounded exactly like the works siren. Thinking it was knocking off time, the complete shop floor rushed to clock off, sending The Bull into a rage at the mass 'defection.'

# LASTING ROYAL LANDMARK

THEY built things to last back in the fifties. The Queen's Coronation in 1953 saw Motherwell Bridge provide its home town with an enduring monument of the occasion, a triumphal arch across the Motherwell-Hamilton road near the Clyde Bridge (which many decades earlier was also built by the company). The deceptively slender-looking edifice, one of many erected in London as part of the Coronation celebrations, caught T.R. Miller's fancy and he had an arch brought North and erected, before gifting it to Motherwell and Wishaw Town Council.

Although originally intended to be on show for a matter of weeks down south, the arch was a popular landmark. It remained on site for many years before finally being removed because of corrosion. Not many people know the arch was actually an amalgam of two triumphal arches, three of the spans being supplemented by a fourth from a second arch. It was also surprisingly heavy because its lower sections had been filled with concrete. Erecting - and later dismantling it - was a much more difficult feat than Motherwell Bridge had anticipated.

For the Coronation, Motherwell Bridge also made a special donation to the employees' social and recreation club. It also gave a Coronation bonus amounting to 10 per cent of annual salary to key company officials.

CORONATION ARCH. T. R. Miller had one of the many triumphal arches, raised in London as part of the 1953 Coronation celebrations, brought to Motherwell and erected on the Motherwell Hamilton Road at the Motherwell end. It was duly presented to Motherwell and Wishaw Town Council. In 1969 the arch was dismantled as corrosion had taken its toll.

A clock tower at the Motherwell Civic Centre was gifted by the company in token of its long association with the Motherwell area.

# A Decade of Change

For Motherwell Bridge, the 1960s could be characterised as the watershed years. The company embarked upon the most radical programme of change in its entire history. In the opening year of the decade it also finally and irrevocably broke with the past, discontinuing the manufacture and erection of steel bridges and other structural work.

There were to be many other breaks with tradition as Ronald Miller sloughed off historical company roles to push Motherwell Bridge to the forefront of international engineering and embrace modern business methods in an era which, itself, was ripe for change.

It was the Swinging Sixties, a decade of great self-confidence within Britain which saw the flowering of the youth revolution and a jettisoning of old ideas for new. Industry and commerce, if a little more sedately, were swept along on the tidal wave of enthusiasm for modernity and better business methods. Companies embraced new ways of organising themselves, with consultancy firms brought in to streamline production lines, production flow, space management and staff deployment. Motherwell Bridge was no exception.

Ronald Miller, by no stretch of the imagination, could be said to be a child of the Flower Power age. But as the new man in control of Motherwell Bridge he realised he had inherited a company which had to chart a new trading direction for itself - one which attempted to overcome the 'boom and bust' cyclical nature of heavy engineering. After the good years of the fifties, the bottom had dropped out of the tankage market, the company's traditional mainstay. Between 1958 and 1960 tankage tonnages more than halved from 46,800 to 19,800 as oil companies started to shop internationally. With steel accounting for 75 per cent of contract costs, the oil giants gravitated naturally to 'home-produced' steel in foreign countries because it was cheaper than imports. While tankage still remained Motherwell Bridge's most profitable line, because of the company's expertise and the many technological improvements it introduced, on its own it could no longer be relied upon to carry the works oncosts and keep it fully occupied throughout the year.

Trying to defend the company position in contracting traditional markets, or those which were ultra-competitive, wasn't going to be enough. What was needed was a new strategy, one which saw diversification of product lines, the capturing of important niche markets in specialist work where the competition was less fierce (and profit margins correspondingly more realistic). That meant streamlining production methods, re-organising the works lay-out, the installation of new machinery to handle technically sophisticated and much more complex orders, and a complete re-vamping of the company's organisational structure. Given the toughness of the financial climate and in the early sixties the company's continuing, and not easily quantifiable, commitments to Hunterston, it was a bold blueprint for the future. But Ronald Miller was determined to bring in new methods - and just as importantly, new blood.

In that, he was following his late father's instincts. In the fifties, prior to his death, T.R. Miller, keenly conscious of the general age level of the Board, had been anxious to recruit younger directors. Indeed, after raising the issue on several occasions at Board meetings, an attempt was made by him to recruit Sir William Lithgow, who declined because of already heavy business commitments. The company was still casting around for suitable appointments when within the space of 15 months its three most senior directors died.

In January, 1958, an ailing David C. Young, who had been with the company for 58 years, 23 of them as a director and around 25 years as general manager, died.

In September of the same year the company lost T.R., to be followed, in January, 1959, by the death of another stalwart, John W. Pearson, who had very shrewdly advised on company investments. At virtually a single stroke, when the company was facing the biggest financial and technical challenges of its existence, Ronald Miller found himself denied the cool and experienced counsel of three men who knew the business inside out. He was determined it wasn't going to happen again.

OIL REFINERY. One of many refineries that benefited from Motherwell Bridge's expertise in the shutdown, overhaul and refurbishment of major petrochemical installations.

In streamlining company operations, based on the advice of the best business and financial brains around, he planned to give a new generation of Motherwell Bridge management their head as directors of a series of subsidiary companies, each devoted to their own specialist activities.

In 1960, with the shareholders' backing, Ronald Miller began the process of diversification by creating Motherwell Bridge (Holdings) Ltd., with Motherwell Bridge & Engineering becoming its wholly owned subsidiary. The senior Board comprised of himself as chairman and managing director; Forbes Masterton as financial director and Sir Arnold Lindley. On the subsidiary Board of Motherwell Bridge & Engineering were Ronald Miller as chairman and managing director,

Forbes Masterton as financial director and two new outside appointments, Inverness-born Nigel McLean, as assistant managing director, and Walter Kohring as technical advisor to the Board (within the year he was to become its technical director). The Holdings company was to act as an investment and acquisitions 'clearing house', investigating potential markets and ideas, formulating Group policy and overseeing the new company Divisions which were to be set up.

The Divisions were being created specifically to capture new markets in activities reasonably closely associated with Motherwell Bridge's normal field of operations. They were also chosen to capitalise on the new skills and advanced technical knowledge which had steadily accumulated in Motherwell Bridge.

**SUBMARINE HULL SECTIONS.** Hull sections being loaded out from the company's Clydeside facility. These units weighed some 800 tons each and were destined for VSEL's Barrow shipyard to be joined up into a Trident submarine. The sections were prefabricated at the Motherwell works and assembled at the Clydeside Yard. Most of the Royal Navy nuclear submarines have hull sections made by the company, the exception being the Dreadnought. Some conventional submarines also received Motherwell Bridge's engineering expertise.

# Heat Exchangers Launch

THE 1960s saw Motherwell Bridge use its new technology build-up during the Hunterston years to break into the field of heat exchangers, through the creation of Motherwell Bridge Thermal Ltd. In June, 1962, it formally launched the new company, establishing a major fabrication works at Uphall, near Broxburn.

It was a double launch celebration. At the hand-over of the premises by Scottish Oils Ltd., Ronald Miller signed a licensing agreement with Foster Wheeler and announced one of the first orders, a £15,000 contract to manufacture ten heat exchangers for use by Courtaulds to separate gases in production of synthetic fibre. MB Thermal's main customers, though, were the petrochemical industries. Motherwell Bridge was the first engineering company in Britain to set up specialised facilities for large-scale production of conventional shell and tube heat exchangers in mild and special steels. Its customised plant attracted considerable interest - and orders - from the petroleum and chemical industries because of fast turn-around times. In some instances Thermal was twice as fast as its competitors in fabricating heat exchangers - while not compromising on quality. It also made condensers and other parts for heat transfer plant.

The company rapidly built up a skilled workforce of 300 at

HEAT EXCHANGER. A double tier shell and tube heat exchanger being prepared for shipment.

Uphall. Within the first year of operations it built all the heat exchangers for a new BP refinery at Westernport, Australia, a Foster Wheeler contract which earned it £300,000. Other big orders included £100,000 worth of high pressure exchangers for a new ICI ammonia plant at Billingham and work at BP's refinery at Llandarcy. Three other contracts worth almost £500,000 to supply heat exchangers for a major expansion at Esso Petroleum's refinery at Fawley, Shell International's new refinery at Teesport and a major export order for a chemical plant in Poland, brought Thermal record levels of business.

Despite fat order books, the early years of trading in a troubled UK financial climate were tough.

Thermal introduced nightshift working to enable it to offer a 'fast response' service for clients.

TUBE SHEET. Welding titanium tubes to a titanium tube sheet in the clean area at Uphall for a North Sea platform heat exchanger.

Like the rest of Motherwell Bridge, in the mid-seventies it benefited greatly from the North Sea oil boom, returning record profits which at their peak topped £1.1 million. Thermal remains today a leading UK player in thermal/mechanical design and fabrication of heat exchanger equipment in an extensive range of specialist steels and alloys and is a highly important sector of Motherwell Bridge's trading.

While principally these new skills arose out of servicing the Hunterston contract, they were not exclusively so. Ronald Miller embarked upon a deliberate policy of building up a strong technological team which could handle highly sophisticated work. Breaking into, and maintaining, a foothold in the new markets being contemplated meant potential clients had to be assured that Motherwell Bridge already had the talent available in-house.

There was considerable flexibility built into the new structure. The new Divisional companies were to be given their own Boards of young and enthusiastic executives, reporting back to the Holdings Board. They had to present their own budgets and work within them. In the new set-up, it would be fairly straight-forward to separate the successful subsidiaries from the non-profitable. It would also, it was hoped, answer the perpetual challenge faced by all managements of large companies: how to keep its management teams from becoming too remote from the workforce.

Almost a decade later, Ronald Miller was to clearly define the objectives of Motherwell Bridge in a Group policy statement, which included the following goals:

- To aim for a sure and safe return upon capital, rather than go for large profits if it meant too great a risk - excluding small individual projects on which risks could be taken without having any major effect upon the Group as a whole;

- In the making of profits, Motherwell Bridge must respect the rights of individuals in the company and the dignity of the company itself;

- A profit from the Group is not sufficient. Each Division, individual section or company must show a profit or a good reason for its existence.

There was one other proviso: Motherwell Bridge would not engage in major work of an experimental or pioneering nature. The company had learned, as on the Hunterston contract, that being first to carry the baton round the running track wasn't necessarily profitable. While the policy statement was penned in 1969 as a distillation of the decade's events, it could equally have applied to its beginning; it mirrored very much Ronald Miller's original vision of change.

Remodelling the trading ethos of a long-established company is a somewhat ponderous affair. Like a great ocean liner altering course, it takes time to turn around. However, time was a luxury Ronald Miller didn't really

## LIKE A ROLLING STONE...

THE most ancient artefact discovered at Motherwell Bridge during site clearances in 1945 was a massive granite block surviving from the Ice Age. According to geological experts it was borne millions of years ago by slow-moving glaciers from the head of Loch Fyne, Argyllshire, to Motherwell, where it was finally deposited in boulder clay at North Motherwell Farm, upon whose original grounds the company is built.
It was discovered during excavations to level the site.
T.R. Miller had its history engraved on the stone.
It had to be moved in the early sixties because of works extensions. It is now outside the company HQ's canteen building.

have: arising from Hunterston he already had a big pool of technological and design talent. His experts weren't going to stick around long if he didn't engage them in new and interesting projects which advanced their careers. American consultants were brought in to check out the first fields for product expansion which the company were considering - the manufacture of heat exchangers and an entree into the world of desalination plants.

To the logical mind of Ronald Miller, there was no more precious resource in the world than water. Heat exchangers cut down on its consumption; desalination plants created potable fresh water for arid regions. He was putting down a marker for the future. In the years to follow the company's own executives scoured the world for suitable trading opportunities, joint ventures and acquisitions. It was a time of constant activity and constant 'crystal ball' gazing as the company sought to divine in which field the need for their services would be greatest.

The speed at which Ronald Miller and his new team of executives 'turned around' the company can be judged from the following statistics. In the seven-year period between 1958 and 1965, Motherwell Bridge spent £1.25 million on capital equipment. Over the same period the number of employees rose from 870 to 1,300. By the end of 1965, Ronald Miller was to announce that virtually every senior position in the Group was occupied by a new executive. It was less of an expansion than a controlled explosion.

Motherwell Bridge was blossoming out in all directions, seizing opportunities wherever they arose. It also re-equipped itself to establish, by the mid-sixties, one of the most modern fabrication plants anywhere in Europe.

Notwithstanding its strictures to stay out of large-scale experimental endeavours, it was still trail-blazing, even in its traditional sectors. With the company's newly acquired knowledge of special steels and welding procedures, the works was building storage tanks of 260 feet diameter, the largest ever built in Britain, and among the biggest in the world. They were capable of holding nearly 600,000 US barrels of oil, more than double the capacity of the old tanks.

Having constructed for itself a giant new 3,000-ton press, the works was also handling thicknesses of steel of up to 9.5 inches (hot pressed) and 4 inches (cold pressed), an engineering capacity which gained it an extremely important avenue of business providing the hull plates in

## END OF LONDON'S ENGINEER'S ROW

IN 1960 a little bit of British industrial history came to an end with the demise of what was known as London's Engineer's Row - Victoria Street, Westminster.

For 52 years the London headquarters of Motherwell Bridge had been situated in the street. The company was one of the very first engineering firms to move there in 1908, at a rental of £30 a year. Motherwell Bridge was soon joined by scores of other important engineering firms.

However, in April, 1960, the company had to move to 23 Princes Gate, Knightsbridge, because much of the street, including its office block, was due for demolition and redevelopment.

Britain's nuclear submarines. Apart from Dreadnought, Motherwell Bridge did work on all nuclear submarines commissioned by the Royal Navy, including Polaris, Trident and Trafalgar class. When Vickers was hit by labour troubles and forced to sub-contract naval work, the Motherwell company built the outer shell of one complete Trident submarine and about half of another. Much of Motherwell Bridge's later work on Britain's nuclear fleet was undertaken out of John Young's Clydeside facility - with the workforce being ordered to conceal it under canvas every time a Russian merchant vessel made port. The exacting specifications of MoD work presented Motherwell Bridge with no problems because the company's welding techniques for thick steels and special alloys were among the best.

At the other end of the spectrum Motherwell Bridge was mass-producing smaller, relatively simpler pressure vessels for use in industry.

Its design and technology teams were also well to the fore, providing specialised testing services (destructive and non-destructive) for clients around the world. They were also charting likely developments coming up on the engineering and industrial horizon.

**MAIN PICTURE: SUBMARINE SECTIONS.** Submarine hull sections being assembled at the company's riverside facility on the Clyde at Glasgow. In the foreground is a vessel with two sections already loaded for transportation.

Units were prefabricated at the Motherwell works and assembled into larger units within weatherproof tanks in Glasgow. The roofs are removable to allow the positioning of the next tier. The weight of the maximum section handled at this facility was 1,200 tons.

INSET: One of the Royal Navy's Trafalgar class nuclear submarines undergoing trials, before deployment at the Faslane Base, on the west coast of Scotland. Motherwell Bridge has fabricated major hull sections for all nuclear submarines since 1962.

Through concentrated research in fields such as cryogenics (the storage of extremely low temperature liquid gases), special alloys and high integrity pipework, the company was always readying itself for the next technological or metallurgical jump in response to the constantly changing needs of the petro-chemical industry and other closely associated markets. That research and development facility was to give Motherwell Bridge a lead over many of its competitors.

RIGHT: PRESSURE VESSELS. Three thick wall pressure vessels for BP Villages offshore gas fields. These liquid measuring drums were fabricated from 9% nickel steel due to its suitability for use at very low temperatures. The vessels are 35mm thick, 612mm inside diameter and some 1800mm long.

BELOW: PRESSURE VESSEL. This pressure vessel is one of the largest and heaviest to be fabricated recently. Measuring 68 metres in length and weighing over 230 tonnes, it was loaded onto a roll on/roll-off ship which sailed from the Clyde to Peterhead on the east coast of Scotland. On the last leg of its journey it travelled by road from Peterhead to Mobil's St Fergus terminal.

As early as 1962 Motherwell Bridge was confidently building the largest rail tank car on two axles ever to run on British Railways track - a massive bulk carbon dioxide transporter, the first of eight it designed and manufactured for a company called Storage and Transport Systems Ltd.

By 1966, it was building double walled storage tanks capable of holding 80 million cubic feet of liquid oxygen at a temperature of minus 183 degrees C, part of £1 million worth of orders in refrigerated storage in the first six months of that year. The contracts came from far and near, and included four low temperature ammonia storage tanks for a terminal in Mexico.

With the extraction of North Sea gas still relatively in its infancy, the company was also heavily engaged in the conversion of the gas industry from coal retorts to naptha cracking. It involved the company in production of tanks, pressure vessels, pipework, refrigeration and storage tanks. Cracker plants, with a life of some 10 years, were used to enrich gas up to 1,000 British Thermal Units. When the much richer North Sea gas, which didn't require such treatment, started coming onshore around 1964 the market gradually was phased out. The company, though, was still doing good business in the manufacture of spheres and pressure vessels, particularly for Wales.

There was no let-up, though, in the pace of rapid company expansion. At times the speed of change occasioned the Group growing pains as it struggled to keep its organisational structure in line with fast-moving developments and the establishment of a blizzard of new companies and joint ventures, each tackling their own special niche areas.

By the end of 1966, Motherwell Bridge had successfully moved into: plant hire of cranes, air compressors, generating and welding plant and heavy lifting gear, initially arising out of Hunterston surplus (Motherwell Bridge Plant Hire, set up in 1961); heat exchangers, evaporators, condensers and other thermal plant (Motherwell Bridge Thermal, set up on its own site at Uphall, near Edinburgh in 1962); desalination plants worldwide (Aqua Chem International Ltd., a joint venture with Aqua Chem Inc. in association with Cleaver-Brooks of America and Marshalls of Gainsborough, set up in 1962); a public health Division covering refuse disposal and incineration plants (Motherwell Bridge Tacol Ltd, operating under licence from Vereinigte Kesselwerke A.G. of Düsseldorf, Germany, established in 1966).

Inside the engineering company, itself, was formed the important Construction and Projects Division to mastermind turnkey projects and highly specialised engineering developments in the field of bulk storage of liquids and gases. Another of the companies which was

to yield impressive results was a joint venture company, Motherwell Byard (later to become a wholly owned subsidiary, Motherwell Bridge Pipe Ltd.) which manufactured continuous spiral fusion welded steel pipeline from 16 inches diameter to 80 inches diameter for use by water, gas, oil, steam and sewage utilities.

**HEAT EXCHANGERS.** These shell and tube heat exchangers were supplied to Esso Petroleum's Fawley Refinery at Southampton during 1965.

**BELOW: UPHALL HEAT EXCHANGER PLANT.** Panoramic view of the heat exchanger tube bundle assembly area at the company's heat exchanger facility at Uphall, West Lothian. On the right hand side is a tube bundle being fitted into its heat exchanger shell.

The Holdings company, itself, by the mid-sixties, was linked with something like 25 to 30 finance or technical agreements, through its subsidiaries, to provide a fully international engineering service. The ultra-fast build-up occasioned a fair amount of corporate indigestion as Motherwell Bridge attempted to assimilate change.

One of the recurring problems was unnecessary duplication of work between 'rival' internal companies. Twice the main Board made moves to regulate the situation. In 1965 Motherwell Bridge, from within its own resources, formed EaMCON, a business consultancy which could step in to assist individual Motherwell Bridge companies at low cost - while earning its keep in outside consultancy work.

In 1968 a special Group Management Board was also formed, answerable directly to the Holdings Board for virtually all management functions and most of the Group's interests. It was created to more closely monitor activities and improve efficiency. For the new companies, themselves, the entree into new markets was not achieved without teething troubles; there were learning curves to be gone through, mistakes to be learned from. Nevertheless, the reorientation of the company in such radical form was a major achievement. With a high emphasis on new technology, Motherwell Bridge had successfully re-invented itself.

LIQUEFIED NATURAL GAS TANK. A cryogenic storage tank and process pipework designed and built by Motherwell Bridge at British Gas's Isle of Grain terminal. This storage tank is capable of storing liquefied natural gas at temperatures as low as minus 163 degrees centigrade. The tank is a double wall type measuring 50 metres in diameter and 33.5 metres in height with a capacity of 50,000 cubic metres. The gas when expanded from its liquefied state is equivalent to 1 billion cubic feet. The space between the inner and outer tank is filled with expanded perlite insulation. These plants for storing North Sea gas are far removed from the old gas holder style coal gas plants. The material for the inner tank is 9% nickel steel to withstand the extreme low temperature and avoid brittle fracture. Special welding techniques had to be developed to construct these tanks to the required integrity.

## CASE OF CROCODILE TEARS

TRANSPORT was always a thorny problem for Motherwell Bridge personnel when engaged on foreign assignments in developing countries. But things can't have come much tougher than the Nigerian trip experienced by Chris Fleming-Brown when sent to check over one of three Motherwell Bridge storage tanks which had failed due to operator error at a township on the River Niger.

He arrived at the River Niger in darkness, hoping to reach the township on the other side by car ferry, having been assured by his driver that it would still be running. Naturally it wasn't. The driver decided to sleep in the landrover overnight and cross in the morning. When Chris proposed doing the same, his man said it wouldn't be a good idea for a white man, saying that if he did there was every possibility he wouldn't wake up. He was far better, said the man, to take the personnel ferry across river that night.

The "personnel ferry" turned out to be a hollowed out tree trunk with about two inches of freeboard. It had been fitted with an outboard motor through the bottom, and the hole sealed with a lump of clay which the boatman had to keep working with his hands to prevent it leaking too badly. The sole crew member's task was to act as a look-out, sitting at the prow and shining a torch across the swirling, pitch black waters to warn of floating logs and trees which could easily capsize the boat.

Throughout the mile-wide journey the torch's beam kept reflecting off what looked like twin candles in the water. Chris was about to ask what they were when a pair of the "candles" suddenly blinked and he realised the river was full of crocodiles. Landfall was made in pitch darkness because the town had been hit by a power cut.

There was a bizarre conclusion to the trip. The following morning at the guest house where he was staying Chris ran into another expatriate, who promptly asked him if he would like a cup of tea. Wondering how on earth he had tea in such a remote area, Chris accompanied him to his vehicle. All was revealed when he saw it. His companion was the Brooke Bond sales manager, complete with his little van, teapot, kettle and tea-bags - on a sales drive.

It had been done, also, in the nick of time. The 'boom and bust' cycle in heavy engineering was still very much in evidence. Prices and orders peaked in 1966, only to go into what one major competitor described as a heavy engineering downturn more severe than the depression of the 1930s. Motherwell Bridge weathered the general fall-off in trade better than most by a judicious mix of cost-savings and a policy of stepping up throughput of short-term work, particularly on the fabrication side. In an effort to ensure a larger slice of export work against foreign competition, the company also joined a consortium known as Capital Plants Ltd. in which the other partners were Newton Chambers Ltd., Whessoe Ltd. and Derek Lennon Associates. The combined resources of the new trading alliance allowed it to bid for major export contracts which were then shared among them. Trading alliances of convenience between rival companies had long been a feature of the industry, so it was a fairly logical extension of a situation which, more and more, existed in practice as companies found themselves bidding for a pool of contracts attracting major foreign competition. As it turned its eyes towards the seventies, while not complacent, Motherwell Bridge must have done so with a certain degree of satisfaction. It had put behind it the last of the traumatic Hunterston years, then used its hard-won technological foundation as a springboard into major diversification. It had survived, in 1968 and 1969, two of the roughest trading years in decades which had laid low several well-known engineering names. It was going into the new decade leaner and fitter. Productivity was up. Overheads were down and it had orders worth £4 million for the first quarter of 1970. Ahead of the company lay the prospect of a new buoyancy in trade occasioned by a £225 million expansion by Shell at Stanlow, which was nearing the engineering stage. It was also going to benefit marginally from the British Steel Corporation's £600 million expansion programme for the next five years which was expected to give engineering as a whole a major shot in the arm. Most of all, there was going to be North Sea oil.

MAIN PICTURE: STANLOW REFINERY. Motherwell Bridge built many of the spheres and storage tanks at Shell's Stanlow refinery. This refinery is the largest in the UK.

INSET: MIDDLETON REFUSE INCINERATOR. The Borough of Middleton, Lancashire's municipal waste roller grate incinerator was the first of its design to go into operation in Britain. Built by Motherwell Bridge in 1967, to the VKW of Germany design, it disposes of 8 tons of household waste per hour. These plants were the first automated approach to incineration.

# ON TOP OF THE WORLD

MOTHERWELL Bridge's distinctive logo - a globe of the world sitting on top of a broad, stylised M - was adopted by the company in 1965. The cross-stroke of the M was designed in flowing lines suggesting the shaping or forming of a thick metal plate, one of the core activities of the company. The two legs of the M formed the rams of the press.

The logo met with much favourable comment and was adopted by the Group's many subsidiary companies as the corporate symbol. It was designed by David Woodroff of advertising agency Ross Woodroff Limited, from a sketch made by Peter Fleming-Brown when working in sales promotion.

The world (globe) being cradled by the M of Motherwell Bridge was tilted on its axis at the suggestion of John Crawford when he saw the finished design.

# ROYAL TIP-OFF WASN'T RUBBISH

THE Swinging Sixties didn't just produce Carnaby Street fashions. They also produced rubbish - by the ton. Mr and Mrs United Kingdom were putting almost 20,000,000 tons of it in the bin every year, nearly half of it in paper products. With the move away from coal fires, and increased packaging by shops, local authorities were faced with a major challenge in handling the rapidly changing character of the nation's rubbish. The answer was to move away from landfill disposal and establish incineration plants, which reduced rubbish bulk by almost 90 per cent. There was another advantage, too. With proper anti-pollution controls, incinerators didn't have to be established at long distances from conurbations.

Motherwell Bridge was quick to spot the trend for incineration developing in mainland Europe. In 1965 it established a licensing agreement with Vereinigte Kesselwerke A.G. (VKW) of Düsseldorf to build in the UK incineration units based on the German company's highly successful mechanical furnaces. It took a full year for the company to set up, in 1966, Motherwell Bridge Tacol Ltd. to handle incineration contracts.

But the time taken to properly establish its organisation was time well spent. Through Tacol, Motherwell Bridge built almost half of Britain's incinerators between the mid-1960s and 1970s in what remains one of the most successful diversifications in company history. The very first contract to be won was to build for Greater Manchester, Britain's first municipal refuse incinerator, a £360,000, 8 tons per hour incineration plant for the Borough of Middleton in Lancashire.

DERRIFORD. The company designed and built a clinical waste incinerator at Derriford near Plymouth. This incinerator handles 600 kilograms per hour of hospital waste and generates steam for the hospital's central heating system.

That success was quickly followed by work on the two most prestigious projects in Britain. The first was a £1 million contract for work on Greater London Council's refuse-burning generating station at Edmonton. The £9 million plant, the largest of its kind in the country, was unique in that it was designed to utilise the waste heat to generate £650,000 worth of electricity a year to be sold to the capital's power grid. Motherwell Bridge was brought in to manufacture and install five incinerator units capable of burning 14 tons of rubbish per hour, and participate in the over-all design. But the plant's commissioning was dogged by technical problems and Motherwell Bridge, through no fault of its own, found itself trapped in a complex financial web when the council terminated its contract with the main contractor following a spate of technical difficulties. From completion in 1971 it took nearly seven years to unravel the resultant financial tangle. However, Motherwell Bridge emerged from it with a satisfactory settlement for the large amount of extra work it had incurred, and made reasonable profits on the contract.

It was to be invited back to the Edmonton plant in later years when the North London Waste Authority needed to install new control systems. The upgrading and refurbishment carried out by Motherwell Bridge boosted electricity generation by 2.5 megawatts.

The jewel in the crown,

SHEFFIELD. The Bernard Road, Sheffield, incinerator was an energy from waste plant, capable of producing steam for district heating. The company provided all the grates and handling facilities and Babcock provided the boiler.

The Queen and the Duke of Edinburgh inaugurated Linwood Incinerator during July 1974. Here, Alexander Ronald Miller accompanies the Duke on a tour of the plant.

though, in the sixties, was Motherwell Bridge's second contract which was to build Glasgow's municipal incineration plant at Dawsholm.

In what was a £1.75 million turn-key project, Motherwell Bridge handled everything on the 10-acre site, from civil engineering to installation of Dawsholm's twin, 12 tons an hour rotary drum incinerators. The plant was formally opened by the city's Lord Provost, Donald Liddle, in July, 1970. In its first year of operation it burned almost 150,000 tons of refuse. The success at Glasgow was to lead directly to the company building the 16 tons an hour Linwood incinerator for Renfrew County Council. An award-winning plant for architectural design, it was completed in 1974 and

inaugurated by the Queen and Prince Philip in July of that year.

At Linwood, refuse passed along six giant rolls within the furnace as the refuse was progressively burned out and conveyed down to the grate. Combustion air was fed individually to the base of each roll so that air flow could be altered dependent on the constituents of the refuse. Heat from the processes was used to provide central heating and hot water throughout the plant. The maximum dust content of gas passing into the atmosphere via Linwood's 140 feet stack was kept to 0.2 grains per normal cubic foot.

Across Britain municipal authorities invested heavily in incineration plants, and the field rapidly attracted major competition. Although Motherwell Bridge remained the doyen of the field, it refused to bid on contracts it considered under-priced and also stayed out of fixed price contracts on large capital projects. Tough Government restrictions on local authority spending eventually bit into capital works budgets and by the late seventies the flurry of activity was over. However, in that time Motherwell Bridge had established itself as the major UK player in the field of incineration. Over the period it had built incinerators at Bristol, Wolverhampton, Sheffield and Southampton; and a refuse transfer station at Queenslie, Glasgow.

Its last big contract won in the seventies again broke new ground. Indirectly, it was the Duke of Edinburgh who was responsible for putting Motherwell Bridge onto the contract. On a Royal visit to Linwood, with typical forthrightness, the Duke told Dennis Eaton, director and general manager of Construction and Projects, it was a nonsense burning rubbish when so much of it could be recycled, and mentioned that South Yorkshire was interested in recycling rubbish. Eaton told Crawford who had the remark checked out - and the company went on to win the contract.

At Doncaster, under the auspices of the Government's Department of Environment, Motherwell Bridge developed and built an experimental municipal recycling plant for South Yorkshire Region which was the first of its kind in the country. Being more expensive to run than conventional waste management plants, it eventually fell victim to the cash cuts on local authority spending.

In the late eighties and early nineties Motherwell Bridge returned to waste management, refurbishing and upgrading equipment for municipal authority plant, and designing and installing automatic combustion control systems. In 1996 it completed at Plymouth the country's most modern clinical waste disposal plant, capable of coping safely with "sharps" - plastic syringes and other utensils. Anti-pollution controls are so tight that it is said emissions from the stack are actually cleaner than the surrounding air.

**DAWSHOLM INCINERATOR.** The second incineration contract awarded to the company was to build Glasgow's municipal incineration plant at Dawsholm. The twin, 12 tons an hour rotary drum incinerators burned almost 150,000 tons in its first year of operation. This was a total turnkey project from a grass roots site.

# PIPE DREAM CAME TRUE

ALTHOUGH Scotland converted to North Sea gas in the 1970s there were numerous areas which weren't on the mains supply network. Motherwell Bridge's expertise in spiral-weld pipe in the 1980s led the company to enter an entirely new market - the manufacture of small 600kg and 1 tonne liquified petroleum gas tanks for farms, hotels, small businesses, and also for rural housing.

Technically, there was very little difference between a large 5 feet diameter spiral-weld pipe tube and a small gas tank.

All that was needed was to weld two ends to it. Being capable of producing spiral-weld tubing to any length required, the company was able to 'customise' tank orders, and turn out finished product at considerable speed for clients. These were then installed and regularly topped up by suppliers with deliveries of propane gas, much in the same way as happened with domestic tanks for oil-fired central heating.

Motherwell Bridge adapted its pipe-weld manufacturing process to handle small tank production and soon had a good-going business. It was able to streamline production to such a degree that it became almost a high volume 'assembly line' engineering operation.

As North Sea gas gradually extended its network, demand slackened. But for many years the production of small tanks made a strong contribution to company turnover.

Motherwell Bridge still makes small general use tanks today - in a wide range of sizes.

# CURTAIN RAISER

THE first major order from behind the Iron Curtain was won by Motherwell Bridge in 1965 when it was appointed to supply tankage to a new terminal in Pancevo, in northern Yugoslavia. It received an order for 67 tanks and four spheres. The tanks ranged in size up to 144 feet diameter by 48 feet high, and 23 were fitted with Horton floating roofs. The contract involved 9,000 tons of steelwork and was obtained through Brefcon.

Heavily involved in landing the contract were sales director Harry Porter and overseas sales manager Donald Hynd.

The order coincided with a drive by Motherwell Bridge to

Harry Porter OBE

Donald Hynd

win new business in Hungary, Bulgaria and Rumania, followed by a trade mission to Moscow in 1966.

Doing business behind the Iron Curtain was extremely complex. Sales representatives had to be invited to Communist countries by one of their trade organisations before being issued with travel visas, itself a lengthy procedure. On arrival,

companies couldn't negotiate direct with the end users but had to conduct business with a panel of experts representing each industry.

Sales directors often had to hang around for days, and sometimes weeks, awaiting recall to negotiations. Most of the time they had to spend in their hotels, because travel around the country wasn't permitted.

Despite the difficulties and atmosphere of suspicion, Porter and Hynd brought in good business for the company during the Cold War era. Harry Porter was later awarded the OBE for services to industry, and in 1982 was appointed to the Holding Company board.

# WATER, WATER EVERYWHERE...

DESALINATION work was one of the pipe dreams of Ronald Miller in the 1960s. The Motherwell Bridge chairman reasoned that with growing world industrialisation and increased tourism the need for fresh, potable water in arid countries would steadily increase. The technology and design expertise required for desalination plants was not vastly removed from Motherwell Bridge's own well established experience in building petro-chemical plants.

The company entered the fresh water market in 1961 through a joint venture. Along with American company Aqua Chem Incorporated, Marshall Sons & Co. of Gainsborough, and Mothercat, Motherwell Bridge set up Aqua Chem International (in 1968 it became a wholly owned subsidiary of Motherwell Bridge and was renamed British Aqua Chem). Using American know-how in an already well developed multi-stage flash distillation process, the new

company began bidding for contracts around the world. From the outset, though, it proved a difficult market to penetrate. The expected boom was slow in materialising.

Aqua Chem International cut its teeth on several small distillation units for the Persian Gulf before building a complete desalination plant at Abu Dhabi. Its biggest success in the early years was in 1964 when it won the contract for a £400,000 desalination plant in Malta for the island's Electricity Board. The one million gallons a day produced were pumped from intermediate tanks to a fresh water reservoir several miles away. The contract was very successfully completed.

But despite extensive interest in sea water distillation among Mediterranean countries, further major orders were not easy to come by. Many of the inquiries in the mid-sixties tended to be of a preliminary nature and failed to materialise. The new company often would invest huge man-

hours in preparing designs and quotes - only to have countries decide against going ahead with any project at all.

Tiring of the lack of big contracts, the Americans asked to be bought out. In 1968 they sold out their interests to Motherwell Bridge, leaving it to continue producing desalination plants, under licence. British Aqua Chem, as it was renamed, went on to build a £270,000 desalination plant for Gibraltar, which produced 225,000 gallons a day to meet rising water consumption from a growing tourism industry. In another £80,000 contract, the company built two 80,000 gallons per day plants at the Shell and BP refinery in Sudan. Then came what everyone hoped would be the breakthrough, the Bahamas contract.

Executives at Motherwell Bridge were jubilant when, in 1969 in the teeth of fierce international competition, the Group won a contract to build a £1.8 million desalination plant

DESALINATION PLANT, NASSAU. The £1.8 million desalination plant nearing completion outside Nassau, Bahamas, in early 1971.

DESALINATION PLANT, GIBRALTAR. A multi-stage flash evaporation type desalination unit being installed in Gibraltar. This plant produced over one million litres of water per day.

outside Nassau. The prestigious turnkey project for the sunshine playground of the very rich was the biggest of its kind in the world for many years, and it seemed to Motherwell Bridge that, after years of fighting doggedly to establish itself in the field of desalination, it had finally achieved its goal.

In charge of the project at New Providence in the Bahamas was Neil Dougan, who was tasked with reclaiming the site from a wilderness before he could begin work proper. "When we arrived, there was nothing but scrub," he says.

Because the plant was being sited in the centre of an island, it meant that to gain water supplies the company had to bore through limestone to extract brine from the water table 100 feet down. When the plant was actually up and running a second bore was used to return excess water back to the water table through reinjection wells, sunk to a level of 250 feet.

That was not the only unusual aspect of the job. The installation featured a new design of plant aimed at doubling the gain ratio in terms of energy produced. The design, which involved using copper coated piping instead of iron, threw up a number of problems, one of the biggest being pipe corrosion. It was discovered that the brine was reacting with the copper, causing spontaneous precipitation on steel piping. Conducting detective work from the other side of the world on the basis of reports coming back from the site wasn't the easiest of tasks for Motherwell Bridge's metallurgists, but eventually they came up with the answer. In previous designs, the brine had natural access to iron sulphate from the piping used. In the new design it hadn't. By adding iron sulphate the problem was solved. "The design for the plant was very much ahead of its time, and it took some time to balance each stage of the process," said Neil.

However, without warning the fixed price contract was to turn into a financial millstone for Motherwell Bridge because of a catastrophic 75 per cent rise in the world market price of copper, followed by a steep rise in the cost of nickel - two of the principal metals used in the construction of the two million gallons a day distillation plant. To give some idea of the impact it had on costs, there were some 72,000 cupro-nickel tubes used in the installation.

To gain the Bahamian Ministry of Public Works project, Motherwell Bridge had been forced to enter into a fixed price contract, a policy it rarely adopted on major undertakings. However, at the time it was a buyers' market. Keen competition meant the Bahamians could virtually dictate their terms, knowing that only a handful of large-scale desalination plants were ever built around the world in any decade.

The unprecedented increase in costs of materials also happened at a time when the Bahamas, politically, was embracing the black power movement, and was on somewhat cool terms with the United Kingdom. Motherwell Bridge completed the contract - but at a loss. It was to be the last major water distillation plant built by the company. Changes in technology saw the world move away from flash distillation to embrace another system, known as reverse osmosis, where salt water is pushed at very high pressures through special membranes which remove the salt.

# Black Gold of the North Sea

In the early seventies, in conditions shrouded in utmost secrecy, Motherwell Bridge veteran projects engineer Chris Fleming-Brown was quietly asked to plan and discreetly amass all the material he would need to establish a fully equipped work camp to erect a major oil terminal. The site, he was told, would contain some of the largest oil storage tanks then being built anywhere in the world.

Chris was told nothing of the location, save that it was on an island off the coast of Scotland; that the material might have to be beach-landed, and that the camp, itself, was to be totally self-sufficient. On the instructions of the oil company, not so much as a glass of water was to be asked for from local islanders by the workforce. For months, working away from head office, Chris planned the logistics of the operation. From his own list of contacts he started putting together the eventual workforce that would be needed and organised the purchase and storage of the equipment and supplies to set up the outside squad camp - in what was one of the best kept secrets in Motherwell Bridge's history.

In fact, it was very much a case of the left hand not letting the right know what was happening. Two versions of a construction camp for Flotta had already been plotted out, and shelved. The first was a "single occupancy" room camp conceived by Colin Ronald who had been called back from his international beat to design it; the second was a plan by Motherwell Bridge's then construction manager, Stewart Paterson, for a camp consisting of small caravans. That idea, too, was set aside. Be that as it may, only a small coterie of directors and key personnel knew that the Group was bidding for a contract worth around £2 million to build the Flotta oil terminal in Orkney for Bechtel on behalf of oil giant Occidental. The first, historic landfall of oil in Scotland was about to become a reality.

Long before the news became public, or indeed contracts were finalised, there were a number of secret visits to the Orkneys by Motherwell Bridge personnel. First to make the journey were John Crawford and Malcolm Phillips, then the new managing director of company subsidiary Motherwell Bridge Plant.

Freshly back from the Texas oil show, where Bechtel, on behalf of Occidental, had first revealed their plans for Flotta, it seemed a million miles removed from the stunning opulence of the Houston Astrodome. It was like stepping back a century in time. A long, fogbound trip, the last stage of which involved chartering a boat to take them out to the island, got them as far as Hoy. They stood on its landfall, wondering if their journey had been really necessary. There was nothing to see. Flotta was little more than a mist-wreathed hummock of treeless, empty land rising out of the sea. It was hard to visualise it was an island still with some 80 inhabitants, far less, along with Hoy during the war, a strategic staging post for nearly 10,000 servicemen. Nearby, occasionally visible at low tide, were the rusting remnants of the German Navy's First World War Grand Fleet, scuttled in Scapa Flow. On Flotta, itself, some derelict military buildings remained as the sole reminder of its brief periods of military activity.

But Crawford and Phillips, whatever their eyes told them, knew they were regarding 230 acres of the most valuable piece of real estate in the country. By an accident of geography, an island sold by the Earl of Zetland to a dozen crofters for £20 each in the 1890s, just about the time Motherwell Bridge was being founded, was on its way to becoming a key terminal from which large tankers would ferry vast quantities of North Sea oil to refineries around Britain and Europe.

A nightmarish return journey across the Pentland Firth aboard a specially chartered fishing boat in dense fog brought the Motherwell Bridge pair back to the Scottish mainland. As they thankfully disembarked on dry land after crossing one of the most treacherous stretches of water in the world, they both were well aware that the company

FLOTTA OIL TERMINAL. Two of the largest diameter floating roof storage tanks in Europe. These tanks at Elf Exploration's terminal on the island of Flotta, Orkney, are 373 feet in diameter and some 48 feet high and can each store one million barrels of crude oil. These remained the largest tanks built by the company for many years until the 1990s when two 1.25 million barrel tanks were designed, fabricated and constructed for Zadco on Zirku Island, Abu Dhabi. At the top left are two liquefied petroleum gas tanks.

CHAPTER 10

was getting in on the ground floor of a brand new oil industry - one which was going to offer huge opportunities to any engineering company "tooled up" for its requirements.

The oil boom could not really have come along at a more propitious period for Motherwell Bridge. The seventies were the decade when Motherwell Bridge 'came of age'. Not only had it decisively made the breakthrough from 'metal bashing' to a truly exceptional range of engineering skills and technological talents covering everything from metallurgy to mechanical engineering, instrumentation and electrical work, it had also started consolidating its innovations and policy changes of the sixties to genuinely establish itself as a multi-discipline group of international standing. There was another sea change, too, which became apparent in the 1970s. Gone were the days when the task of pricing contracts was left solely to the accountants. The rigid demarcation of responsibilities, where project management concerned itself with carrying out the work while the autocratic Forbes Masterton and his team handled the financial details, vanished. At one time it would have been unthinkable, but line managers were now expected to be pro-active on contracts. They were expected to have an input into pricing and, on the job, take into account running budgets, implementing cost savings where warranted. The result was a much more involved approach which usually led to better decision-making and greater accountability. The North Sea was a proving ground for many of the new company philosophies and disciplines Motherwell Bridge was imposing upon itself.

Crawford and Phillips were not the last contingent from Motherwell Bridge to make a surreptitious visit to the Orkneys. Later general manager David Syme and construction manager Stewart Paterson, posing as bird-watchers, quietly made their way to the island to check it over, crossing over in a small open boat with one of the Orcadians, who, like all island communities, had a highly efficient grapevine and knew a great deal more than the rest of the world about the strangers regularly coming into their midst. On Flotta, islanders the pair met paid lip service to their 'cover story' of being bird watchers - but very firmly told them ornitholigists' objections would not be welcome: Orkney wanted the oil.

On the bumpy, grass track ride back across Flotta to their boat, the two found themselves sharing the small Ford Anglia taxi with a sheep with an injured leg. The car trip, particularly for the fastidious David Syme, must have been purgatory, for the unkempt animal smelled abominably and its matted fleece seemed to house more than its fair share of ticks.

The seeds for the Flotta deal - eventually won in competition against UK rivals Whessoe and Capper Neill - had been sown almost two years earlier by John Crawford. Along with Malcolm Phillips and Harry Porter, the Group's sales director, he had attended America's annual oil industry show in Houston, Texas.

138

# CHAPTER 10

It may have seemed strange that a Scottish engineering company should have to fly to Texas to find out what was happening on its own doorstep. But Houston was the oil capital of the world. As home to a fabulously wealthy international industry, it was in its boardrooms that decisions involving billions of dollars were taken on the finding and development of oilfields around the world.

To the Americans the North Sea represented a new challenge. It was a foul weather exploration area where men and equipment would be tested to the limit by its harsh environment. It involved developing a whole new technology to cope with the ocean depths involved and

MAIN PICTURE: FLOTTA. The main terminal at Flotta with the additional five, half million barrel storage tanks, ballast tanks and the two LPG insulated tanks and the processing areas in the foreground for Piper and Claymore fields. The company installed large parts of these process areas which de-gas and stabilise the oil brought in from the North Sea fields before it is shipped out for further refining.

BELOW: FLOTTA. The jetty at Flotta where tankers off-load their ballast and take on vast quantities of crude oil.

the enormous stresses to which rigs and equipment would be exposed in often mountainous seas. Unprotected, a man would die within minutes in its waters from hypothermia. Indeed, most fishermen sailing the North Sea's icy wastes never bothered to learn to swim, reckoning it to be a waste of time. The prize, though, when the extraction difficulties were overcome was a rich one: millions of barrels of high grade crude which commanded top dollar.

Uninvolved in the exploration of the southern sector of the North Sea, where British companies like Shell were already well established extracting natural gas, the Americans were the first to explore for oil in the northern sector. In Scotland, though, back in 1970-71, it still seemed a slightly unreal situation. There was an air almost of disbelief that a large-scale oil industry was going to evolve off its coastline. In the absence of any heavy American presence in the North of Scotland, the public had difficulty in perceiving Scotland as an oil-rich nation.

That perception was to change radically in the years that followed which were one of the most febrile periods of post-war Scottish political history. Politics and an explosion of North Sea activity coalesced throughout the seventies in a country-wide upsurge of nationalism culminating in 1979 in a referendum over whether Scotland should have its own devolved Parliament, called a Scottish Assembly. In the years running up to one of the most vigorous and passionate political debates since the war, the Scottish Nationalist Party coined the decade's most potent political slogan: It's Scotland's oil. It was a sentiment, naturally enough, which didn't carry much weight with the Americans who had paid for the exploration and extraction rights.

Nevertheless, mindful of the political sensitivities of the United Kingdom and the local communities in Scotland, whose support would have to be gained to develop on-shore facilities for handling and processing North Sea oil, from the outset the consortium of oil interests took care not to ruffle unnecessarily any feathers. The strictures on self-reliance, as at Flotta, were just one of those precautions. It was an unnecessary one, as it turned out. The Orcadians welcomed the terminal, which earned the islands 2p per tonne handled by Flotta. The terminal encountered the least opposition of any North Sea oil development anywhere in Scotland; there wasn't

even a public inquiry over the plans. The islanders were also tolerant of the more colourful antics of the free-spending 'bears,' as the construction crews were called, passing through Kirkwall and Stromness as they came off-site to fly home on leave. Any complaints the 'bears' made tended to be pretty direct in nature. On one occasion in a Kirkwall hotel, irked by the toughness of the steaks they had been served up, they used them to play hopscotch!

However, long before the public's imagination was fired by the North Sea's 'black gold', Motherwell Bridge's John Crawford had been discreetly searching for an entree into the fledgling North Sea offshore oil industry. He had watched with interest the development of natural gas in the southern sector of the North Sea through the latter part of the sixties, and as early as 1971, the Group had been quietly casting around for suitable sites with good marine facilities. It knew these would be essential for fabricating some of the large rig installations needed for offshore North Sea oil exploitation. The company had already bid for some of the south sector rigs without success, there being a preference at that time by the industry to get shipyards to build them.

OFFSHORE EXHIBITION, HOUSTON. John Anderson dressed in Highland costume posing with two models at the Offshore Technology Conference in Houston, Texas.

Nevertheless, that wasn't always going to be the case. Crawford wanted to check out what was happening with the Americans. So to the oil show in Texas went Motherwell Bridge's team. They took on a 10 square feet stand unit and set out their wares in the Houston Astrodome complex. True to the Texan reputation for being larger than life, the scale of the show was incredible. It was a Hollywood-style extravaganza where the entertainment began at lavish and worked its way up the ladder to spectacular. The greatest spectacles of all were the events staged in the Celestial Suite where, for 20,000 dollars a night, companies could rent out one of three huge suites, each done out in different historical themes.

# THE 'INVISIBLE' £3 MILLION CONTRACT

DURING the early North Sea years Motherwell Bridge gained a £3 million contract at Dalmeny, Firth of Forth, to construct seven massive new inland reception tanks for oil pumped down from Cruden Bay, Aberdeenshire. Land-owner Lord Primrose, chairman of the Jockey Club, insisted that the tanks be sited so that they were invisible from any road - which is why today they can only be seen by the public when flying out of Edinburgh airport. An eighth tank was added ten years later.

Throughout the seventies, Motherwell Bridge found itself constantly having to acquire new facilities to cope with the volume of work it was doing for the North Sea. In 1972, with the development of the BP Forties and Auk fields imminent, the Group leased from Robb Caledon on a temporary basis their disused deep water facilities at Burntisland in Fife. With 80 feet lock gates, the site gave good access for large barges onto which the bigger constructions could be loaded.

When the barges for some of the components grew even bigger, the company moved along

TANKAGE AT DALMENY. The company designed and erected seven, half-million-barrel crude oil floating roof storage tanks and associated fixed roof tankage at BP's Dalmeny terminal. The River Forth with its striking landmarks, the Forth Rail Bridge and the much newer Road Bridge are in the background.

the coast to Edinburgh's port of Leith, where it leased a 20-acre site from the Forth Ports Authority. The Group committed £1 million capital to establish an important marine fabrication facility there over a period of two years. The acquisition at Leith was an important development because it increased the size of fabrications which could be sent out to the oilfields. Overflow work went to a site at Grange Dock, Grangemouth, where Motherwell Bridge built, among other fabrications, a large buoyancy sphere and leg sections for a production platform.

Throughout the decade, Motherwell Bridge's various divisions were heavily involved in North Sea work. It took on new premises in Motherwell where pipe fabrication was established, constructing North Sea platform modules. Additional work space also had to be taken locally. In Wales, for a three-year period between 1973 and 1976, the company also operated a marine facility yard in Swansea.

North Sea development acted as a catalyst across the whole spectrum of oil industry work. For much of the decade the whole of the UK oil and gas industry was buoyant. Milford Haven, Nigg Bay, Kent and Grangemouth all provided major tankage contracts for Motherwell Bridge in addition to work on Flotta and Sullom Voe.

There, staff dressed in period costume ministered to guests' every needs at quite awesome banquets.

The night that Motherwell Bridge attended the Celestial Suite as guests of Ingersoll Rand, for whom the company held a major UK distributorship, the theme in one area was the French court of Louis XIV; in another a Roman banquet. It was corporate entertaining on a level which beggared belief. Indeed, the whole show was a monument to the wealth generated by a global industry. In the astrodome, as far as the eye could see, were superb stands, each lined with stunningly beautiful girls and all manner of entertainments to attract businessmen into their exhibitions.

"The magnitude of it was simply mind-boggling," Malcolm Phillips recalls. "In the astrodome itself there must have been two fixed wing aircraft and at least four helicopters on display and every stand seemed to have girls on duty who could have stepped straight from the pages of a fashion magazine. For the first time you got an inkling of the sheer size and power of the market. It simply took your breath away."

Motherwell Bridge's stand may have paled somewhat in the face of such an onslaught of corporate opulence, but what it lacked in size it certainly made up for in ingenuity. The company put on display a giant whisky bottle and asked businessmen to drop their business cards into it - saying that the first name picked out of the bottle would win its gallon of whisky. That, and the kilted figure of the then marketing manager John Anderson on the stand, proved an instant draw. The cards came flooding in, giving the company a speedy - and as it turned out valuable - prospective mailing list. One businessman was so impressed that he came up to the stand and offered to pay Motherwell Bridge 3,000 U.S. dollars on the spot for the chance to photo-copy every card in the bottle.

The biggest pay-off, though, came when an oilman arrived on the stand and asked Harry Porter if the company could build oil storage tanks in Scotland. Porter evinced some surprise that anyone was interested in building tankage in Scotland, but the inquirer assured him it was certainly going to happen, although the location was still top-secret. They were looking for a company capable of building 350 feet diameter storage tanks with a capacity for one million

barrels - then the largest being made in the world.

Within 24 hours, Crawford and Porter were sitting in the Houston offices of Bechtel, who acted on behalf of Occidental, hearing of the plans for the first Scottish terminal for North Sea oil. On their return to Scotland, the planning for Flotta began. Right up to the final bid, total secrecy was maintained. Stewart Paterson remembers the telex message coming in from Bechtel and Occidental, confirming that Motherwell Bridge had won the contract. "Even then they didn't mention Flotta by name because there was still planning permission required," he recalls. When the contract was finalised, the first order was for five massive storage tanks, 48 feet high, 270 feet in diameter, and each capable of holding 500,000 barrels, then the largest in Europe. That order was later supplemented with a second contract to build a further nine storage tanks, two of them with a capacity of one million barrels. The official announcement that Motherwell Bridge had won the major tankage contract for the £15 million terminal at Flotta was made in January, 1974, and work commenced in May of that year. As ever, transport to the remote site verged on the unconventional. Men and materials were ferried in on a Para Handy-style puffer, the Lady Isle, which had been resurrected

## CHICAGO BRIDGE LINK ENDS

NORTH Sea oil finds brought to an end a little piece of history. The long and profitable link-up between Motherwell Bridge and the Chicago Bridge Company ceased when in 1973, the American company announced that it was not renewing its licensing agreement for the fitting of floating roof storage tanks - because it wished to enter the United Kingdom tankage market.

Under the agreement, Chicago Bridge had excluded itself from bidding for UK business. It was an amicable break-up of a trading partnership which had endured for 40 years.

by Motherwell Bridge from a boatyard on the Scottish mainland. She was no thing of beauty, and required considerable renovation, but she was sound - and as tough and serviceable as any of the generations of puffers which had plied their trade along the Scottish coastline for generations. Skippered by a captain, with a lady companion and a large alsatian dog as 'crew,' the Lady Isle was also used to ferry the work squads, fresh water and fuel for the camp generators. On more than one occasion a Flotta work squad would find themselves on board when the Lady Isle ran aground in foggy weather. But with the hardiness of her breed, she could settle easily on the bottom and float off unharmed at high tide. She operated on the run for two years before being replaced by speedboats. Then she was sold off to ply her trade in the Persian Gulf, a most unlikely locale for such a venerable lady.

At Flotta Chris Fleming-Brown and his outside squad built the construction camp before the fabrication teams went on to erect every storage tank sited on the island. On such an exposed site, high winds posed a number of technical challenges. Realising that, on their own, the half erected walls of the storage tanks wouldn't withstand some of the fierce gales they could expect, Motherwell Bridge followed a 'roof first' method of fabrication. Normally the last part of erection, the roofs were prepared first. Raised gradually inside the structure as the walls were being built, the roofs acted as circular buttresses, giving additional rigidity and strength to the segments being built around them. It was an ingenious solution and one which saw the tanks successfully withstand the worst of the winter storms during construction. Only once, during extreme gales, did they have a few plates blown down.

**SULLOM VOE OIL TERMINAL.** Motherwell Bridge built 32 storage tanks at the Sullom Voe terminal in the Shetland Islands. In addition the company carried out a considerable amount of mechanical, electrical and instrumentation work on the terminal.

At the height of the contract, something like 250 men were working on-site, but far from all of them were involved in tankage. Motherwell Bridge had a large contingent undertaking the electrical and mechanical work for the terminal, which was considerable. Among the elements the company constructed were the fire water jetty, the flare area, the compressor house, where gases were compressed and liquefied, and many other major mechanical works built upon the island.

The contract for that sector of the work was finalised with Occidental in a London steakhouse one Sunday afternoon by the company's Neil Dougan - the same steakhouse, incidentally, where three of the world's richest men, Paul Getty, Armand Hammer and Lord Thomson of Fleet over lunch had taken the original decision to form their consortium to develop the Piper Field. Legend has it that not one of the trio was carrying enough money to pay for their modest meal; they almost got thrown out until someone recognised who they were.

The Flotta contract is remembered with much affection by Stewart Paterson, who says that the Americans who worked with them were the genuine roughnecks - larger than life characters who brought colour and vitality onto the site. Not that the UK squads were any slouches when it came to having an appetite for life. Paterson remembers the lengths the men went to when they wanted to stage a dance to celebrate the end of the contract. At St. Margaret's Hope, on the Orkney mainland, the local hotel didn't have enough space to stage one, so the men built a concrete floor extension, put up temporary awnings, and held the dance. "Flotta wasn't like Sullom Voe," said Paterson. "There the entertainment was very organised. Big name entertainers like Billy Connolly regularly came up. But in Orkney you had to make your own amusement."

The storage terminal at Flotta, to which crude was pumped from the Piper and Claymore fields 150 miles away through a £40 million pipeline, was officially opened by Labour's Energy Secretary of State, Tony Benn, in January, 1977. But long before work on the site even commenced Motherwell Bridge was already gearing up for many other aspects of North Sea work, off-shore and on-shore.

Since the beginning of 1974 the company's sights were firmly fixed on Sullom Voe, in Shetland, where Europe's largest oil terminal was being planned at a cost which eventually topped £1.2 billion. Competition was fierce, but Motherwell Bridge's reputation gained it a £30 million slice of the action in tankage construction and other installation works which, for the company, were to last four years. Getting in on the ground floor at Sullom Voe brought to more than a few executives in Motherwell Bridge a sense of relief. The company's commitment to winning contracts there was total. Contemplation of failure simply wasn't an option. "The attitude was: this is Scotland. We have to get it," says John Crawford. Thus Motherwell Bridge joined the ranks of key companies in Shetland - a list which even at that stage was beginning to resemble a Who's Who of British engineering.

RIGHT: FRACTIONATING COLUMN. One of a number of fractionating columns fabricated at Motherwell and shipped to Sullom Voe. The company entered the unfired pressure vessel market in the late 1940s. This expertise later enabled the company to enter the nuclear market. Heavy wall pressure vessels remain an important market today.

BELOW: SULLOM VOE. The company designed, supplied and erected 16 half million barrel floating roof crude oil storage tanks at Sullom Voe.

# No More Tears from 'Bubbly' Young

ONE of the most notable company acquisitions of the seventies by Motherwell Bridge was the take-over of John Young & Co. (Kelvinhaugh) Limited. Founded more than a century ago in Glasgow, and with company operations in Sheffield and Port Talbot, it is one of the best-known engineering names in Britain.

It was known, universally, as 'Bubbly' Youngs, the nickname being a reference to the founder, John Young, who was known as 'Bubbly ' to one and all because, as the Scots say, "he was aye greetin'." He was the sort of boss who, literally, would throw down his cap in a rage and jump on it, if a job wasn't going to his satisfaction.

While involved in mechanical plant construction, plant and labour hire and machinery installation, John Young & Co. was famed for its heavy lifts expertise. It was the biggest crane operator in Scotland. Whenever there was an especially tricky, heavy or delicate lift involved it was to Youngs that British industry turned. With its specialist cranes and wealth of experience, it carried out many of the most difficult removals, relocations and machinery installations in the United Kingdom. Its clients ranged right across the spectrum of heavy industry, from steel plants and shipping companies to distilleries and the pharmaceutical industry. It remains a top player in the UK to this day.

Its acquisition in 1976 was a source of satisfaction to Motherwell Bridge's Malcolm Phillips, who had alerted the Group to changed circumstances in the company's management following the death of one of the Young brothers. Prior to joining Motherwell Bridge, Phillips had worked for seven years at John Young & Co. as assistant to its technical director, Frank Young. Today the company is an important strand of Motherwell Bridge's engineering portfolio.

BUBBLY YOUNG'S. A multi-lift at British Steel's Ravenscraig works involving four mobile cranes and appropriate erection teams. John Young & Co., has a long and widely recognised expertise in the field of special and heavy lifting.

# CHAPTER 10

S ullom Voe - the name from the old Norse, 'sol heimr' means 'a place in the sun' – was an immense undertaking. Motherwell Bridge was one of more than 100 companies involved in its construction. At its peak, in the late seventies, the on-site workforce at Sullom Voe numbered 7,000. More than one million tons of materials poured off ships from the ports of Leith, Grangemouth, Bromborough and Invergordon. Heavy load pre-assembled units weighing up to 480 tons were brought ashore. The logistics of keeping such a vast enterprise in such a remote area supplied with a steady flow of equipment and material were huge.

Accommodation was provided in construction villages and in two floating 'hotels' - the accommodation ships Rangatira and Stena Baltica. The specially built 120 megawatt power station to provide electricity to the site was the largest building on Shetland, with a capacity three times greater than the island's own diesel-fuelled generating station at Lerwick. A wartime airfield was re-opened to supplement Sumburgh airport, 55 miles away, and a 30-mile fast new roadway built to improve its road links with Sullom Voe. Even the very size of Shetland increased as a result of the development. Before work proper could begin on the site, a thick layer of peat had to be stripped from the ground.

A staggering nine million cubic metres of peat were removed at Calback Ness and dumped in nearby Orka Voe in a carefully controlled operation. It extended the land mass of the island by 100 acres.

However, the development of Europe's largest oil terminal did not proceed as straight-forwardly as it had at Flotta. Originally planned only to be a storage and dispatch terminal, it blossomed out into becoming a fully fledged processing plant. In Shetland's case, too, the impact of the oil industry was much greater. A remote island community, famed for its rugged beauty and rare wildlife, such as the Snowy Owl, saw its population swell from 18,000 to 25,000. Not only did it stretch to the limit Shetland's infra-structure resources, it also, to a degree, swamped the local economy. The lure of high wages saw young people, and even a local dentist, move away from traditional employment to the oil industry.

MAIN PICTURE: SULLOM VOE. Due to the adverse weather conditions experienced in the northern islands off Scotland, the company constructed many of the smaller storage tanks for the Sullom Voe project at their Grangemouth facility on the east coast of Scotland. On completion the tanks were loaded onto roll-on/roll-off vessels and transported to Sullom Voe by sea before being manoeuvred into position on site.

INSET: SULLOM VOE. These pipe rack modules were fabricated at the company's Leith facility and were sailed direct from Leith to Sullom Voe.

At the helm of the Shetland council was a chief executive, Ian Clark, who quickly established himself as the oil industry's toughest negotiator. Finding oil, for communities, is a bit like being struck by lightning; they can be left picking up the pieces as the industry moves on to its next development. Clark was well aware of this. Determined to ensure that the Shetland way of life would be both protected and enhanced long-term, he adopted a simple philosophy in all his negotiations: the oil companies needed Shetland more than Shetland needed the oilmen.

His hard-nosed approach paid rich dividends, both in protecting Shetland's fragile ecology and in winning lasting financial benefits for the islands. In adopting that stance he was helped by the need of the oil companies to extract the oil from below the seabed as fast as possible. Middle East nations, through OPEC, were dramatically pushing up the price of oil and the Western powers, fearing they would be held to ransom over their high energy consumption, were keen to develop major alternative sources. Britain's Labour Government, itself mired in a balance of payments deficit, was equally keen to see the oil revenues flowing in. Against that backdrop, the cool Mr Clark tended to get what he wanted. He did a very good job for Shetland, says John Crawford, but Motherwell Bridge didn't find the local authority chief executive unduly difficult to deal with. Clark, himself, had been born virtually within the shadow of the company's cranes at Motherwell and well knew its reputation for top quality work.

The company's tankage contract saw it construct 16 giant floating roof storage tanks on the high ground of Calbeck Ness. Each tank had a capacity of 500,000 barrels, which equated to about half the daily production of the high grade sweet crude from the East Shetland Basin. The tanks were surrounded by safety walls, known as bunds, which in the unlikely event of a tank collapse would contain its oil and prevent widespread pollution. Protective bunds were also built around the terminal's gas tanks. The tanks built by Motherwell Bridge at Sullom Voe were much higher than those in Orkney - 72 feet compared to 48 feet.

## NO HOLES IN THE PROFITS

NOT a single leak! That was Motherwell Bridge's proud boast from the mid-sixties to the late seventies as it manufactured hundreds of miles of mains piping for water authorities across Britain, using a new technique known as spiral fusion weld - or to give it its full Sunday name, automatic submerged arc fusion welding.

The new spiral weld pipe mills produced pipe from a continuous steel strip which was spiralled into shape and immediately welded, internally and externally, as the pipe formed. The method allowed pipes to be produced to any length required at the rate of about one metre per minute. At around one-tenth of the cost of conventional pipe-making plant, the new spiral pipe mills, first developed in Germany, were extremely cost-effective. They were also highly flexible. Operations could be simply programmed to turn out pipes ranging in diameters from 16 inches to 80 inches from coils of half-inch thick steel. The pipes were then lined and coated with anti-corrosion or other protective material, dependent on their use.

Motherwell Bridge was the first large engineering group in the United Kingdom to develop and design its own spiral weld pipe mills for 'made to order' high volume pipe production. It came into the market in January, 1967, purchasing a 50 per cent stake in the Byard company, which had developed spiral weld technology. Renamed Motherwell Byard the company, with its new injection of engineering-based management, produced excellent returns. Its very first contract under the Group banner was to produce 27 miles of 24 inches and 27 inches diameter piling tubes for a jetty at Immingham oil terminal.

But it was Britain's water industry which proved the biggest customer. In Scotland the company manufactured 23 miles of large diameter pipe for the Loch Lomond water supply scheme.
The biggest contract of all was in Glamorgan, Wales, on the massive River Towy scheme aimed at eventually doubling the Welsh water supply. The principal phase of the scheme - later to be officially

SPIRAL PIPE MILL. The spiral mill producing large diameter line pipe for the water industry. The process was a relatively cheap, fast and efficient method of producing large quantities of water pipe compared to conventional pipe making. Strip steel is introduced to the mill at an angle, formed to the pipe diameter and welded inside and outside automatically in a continuous process. The angle, and the width of the strip determine the diameter of the pipe.

inaugurated in May, 1973, by H.R.H. Princess Alexandra - was to supply 86 million gallons a day to the Swansea Valley. Motherwell Bridge produced more than 30 miles of large diameter pipe to link industry to its new supplies, a contract worth £900,000. One of the interesting features of the job was that, for the first time, Motherwell Bridge set up its own complete pipe-making facility near the site. Near-site pipe-making cut costs, did away with transport difficulties and saved time. It also had applications for work abroad. Other major contracts in England in the 1970s included work for Yorkshire, Essex, Anglian and Bristol Water Boards.

The company relocated Byard at its headquarters in Motherwell where it installed a £35,000 spiral pipe mill. A second was constructed at the Group's Sighthill works, Edinburgh for manufacturing 'specials,' bends, Y-pieces and fabricated pipe. The two pipe-making facilities were later sold abroad for £1 million when superseded at Motherwell by a £1 million mill designed and constructed in-house by Jim Prettyman who was the company's general manager.

Spiral weld pipe was suitable for use in many industrial plant processes, but not - unfortunately - in the North Sea. Because of the higher pressures involved, operators preferred to stick with conventionally manufactured pipes to bring oil and gas ashore. However, spiral-weld was a major contributor to the rapid expansion of Britain's water infra-structure. Motherwell Bridge's quality of pipe, and its testing procedures, were so good that never once had it to be called back to a site over leakages.

In the mid seventies, following cut-backs in capital expenditure programmes, the market fell back. Today Motherwell Bridge is still involved in spiral weld, but concentrates its activities principally on providing a specialist service, producing the 'hard to make' pipe sections which require special design features.

In 1980 Motherwell Bridge bought over the whole company, renaming it Motherwell Bridge Pipe Ltd.

SERIES 3,000 PIPE MILL

The huge oil storage capacity was essential so that production from the oilfields could proceed at a steady rate. It did away with the necessity of having a tanker almost permanently docked at some of its four jetties, waiting to take on a load. It allowed the largest of the tankers to be loaded quickly and also built in a comfortable storage margin in the event of delayed arrivals - an important consideration. Although Sullom Voe was a natural harbour sheltered from the worst of the Atlantic gales, in severe weather tankers were unable to dock. In a bad year as many as 73 days could be lost - one day in five.

As a receiving and dispatch centre, Sullom Voe is still a larger oil terminal than anything in Europe (including Holland). The first crude was pumped into Sullom Voe in November, 1978, to be followed in May, 1981, by an official inauguration by the Queen, accompanied by the King of Norway and Prince Philip. It was an event marred by the explosion of a small bomb planted by the IRA in a heating boiler in the new power station about a quarter of a mile from the spot where Her Majesty performed the ceremony. No-one was injured. With her usual sang froid, the Queen ignored the incident.
Nor did it affect Shetland's big day. It is perhaps worth noting that between 1978 and the Queen's Royal visit in 1981, some £7 billion of crude had already been brought ashore, an indication of the wealth being generated by one of the greatest engineering feats in oil exploration of the 20th century.

Motherwell Bridge was to return to Sullom Voe in the decades that followed, carrying out repair and maintenance work. It is still active in Shetland today. With crude being processed now containing greater quantities of sulphurs and corrosive agents, upgrading and renewal of plant now 20 years old has seen the company take on much of the maintenance work. It has total responsibility for all maintenance at the Flotta site, in Orkney.

While Flotta and Sullom Voe were key contracts for Motherwell Bridge, they were only part of a huge range of activity in North Sea development. The company's involvement with the North Sea, right across the board, was considerable. Major structures and assemblies which, until the end of the sixties, had been handled only by shipyards were now coming the way of Motherwell Bridge and a handful of other UK

companies. Heavy engineering began to take on a whole new meaning; where once the industry had routinely used 25-ton mobile cranes and 30-ton derricks, it was finding it was being required to construct, assemble and move structures like temporary decks for platforms in the BP Forties field which weighed up to 1,500 tons each.

BELOW: FABRICATION YARD FOR OFFSHORE STRUCTURES. In the 1970s the company leased 95,000 square yards of storage and construction area within the non-tidal Western Harbour at Leith on the Firth of Forth. The yard's annual capacity for fabrication of offshore modules and structures was 8,000 tons. The company supplied over 50,000 tons of heavy structures to major offshore operators including jackets, modules, flare booms, semi-submersible legs and deck sections.

INSET: OFFSHORE MODULES. These large drilling and wellhead modules were prepared for shipment within the company's open fabrication area at Western Harbour.

# CHAPTER 10

Because of Motherwell Bridge's development of load-out techniques, and the availability of the large, ocean going barges to transport structures, the company's expertise was also in demand for other major offshore installations.

**ALEXANDER DENNIS EATON.**
Dennis Eaton was a civil engineer, educated at Trinity College, Dublin, and in his early career worked overseas. After returning to the U.K. he worked for Dupont before joining Motherwell Bridge to head up the embryo Construction and Projects Division which expanded greatly under his control. He firmly believed in engineers being directly responsible for the financial outcome of their actions, encouraging not only the aim of good profitability but positive cash flow. Dennis retired in 1985 at which time he was a director on the Group Management Board.

**JOHN SCOTLAND MORELAND.**
John Moreland, a BSc Honours graduate from Glasgow University, was employed by Motherwell Bridge at Hunterston in the period 1957-1961, then left to join Stewarts & Lloyds. He rejoined Motherwell Bridge as production manager in 1967 and later headed up the new facility at Leith for fabrication of offshore structures. John left to join the British National Oil Corporation in 1982 at which time he was on the Motherwell Bridge Group Management Board.

The company also undertook extremely complex engineering tasks such as building process modules for Shell Brent A and B; air conditioning, electrics and instrumentation on self-contained drilling packages; complex single-point mooring buoys and nodes for major platform assemblies. It was a multi-discipline approach, where every skill Motherwell Bridge had assembled under its roof, tended to be called into play at a variety of sites.

To handle the huge offshore structures, fabrication yards first at Burntisland (set up and run by Guy Scott) and later at Leith's Western Harbour were established. They were quickly in full production. Leith which had its own office, was run by director John Moreland. Even before the yard officially opened, it was being used as the site for construction of a massive buoyancy sphere for a North Sea Forties field platform to replace a German sphere which had imploded during a flotation manoeuvre.

Every decade throws up executives who drive forward company objectives. It would be fair to say that, in the seventies, Dennis Eaton and John Moreland were two of the key figures implementing management strategy. Eaton, the director responsible for Motherwell Bridge's Construction and Projects Division and Motherwell Bridge Tacol, with his civil engineering background, had been sent to Texas by the company to examine how a local yard handled offshore work. That knowledge was implemented in the setting up of Leith. Moreland's role was to ensure that shop floor production went smoothly, a task he was eminently suited for.

Parallel to all the North Sea work, Motherwell Bridge did considerable work for British Gas, constructing generation modules. Another major contract in the mid-seventies was a £9 million project building a total fuel oil handling facility for the Scottish Hydro Board. A five-year development, involving considerable high quality pipework, it was a textbook project. It started later than equivalent English plants and was completed years ahead of them. That, alone, is perhaps a reflection of the mood of the times; there was a buoyancy and confidence that seemed to reflect in everything Motherwell Bridge touched.

The golden years of oil will for ever remain the seventies. It was the decade when Motherwell Bridge saw all its hard-won new technological skills and re-organisation of the sixties translate into excellent profits. It will be remembered as the most successful decade in the first 70 years of Motherwell Bridge's existence.

# TWO MB GAS TANKS CAN SUPPLY SCOTLAND FOR 10 DAYS

THERE is nothing more disruptive to a country than even temporary loss of its energy supplies. It is one of the reasons power industries build into their networks large-scale extra provision which can 'top up' supplies when demand is exceptionally heavy or be utilised as a single source supply in an emergency. The Glenmavis liquid natural gas facility at Airdrie, Lanarkshire, built by Motherwell Bridge for the British Gas Corporation during the 1970s, is designed with the capacity to supply Scotland's complete mains gas needs non-stop for up to 10 days.

If ever Scotland's North Sea gas supplies were to be severely disrupted, the Glenmavis plant would kick into action, giving engineers probably twice the 'window' they would need in which to carry out even the most major repairs. It seems incredible, but thanks to the science of cryogenics, Scotland's complete gas consumption could be sustained from just two Motherwell Bridge-built double-walled tanks, 150 feet high and 151 feet in diameter, and each holding around 20,000 tons of liquefied gas.

Cryogenics, the science of storing gases in liquid form at very low temperatures, came into its own in the mid-1960s when it was realised that the technique had large-scale storage and transportation applications.

By liquefying gases, industry found it could reduce the storage space needed by as much as 600 times. Simply by lowering the temperature, it was possible to condense 600 cubic feet. of gas into one cubic foot. of liquid. The temperatures required for liquefying ranged from -5 degrees C for butane to -33 degrees C for ammonia, -50 degrees C for propane to -103 degrees C for ethylene, and -163 degrees C for natural gas.

However, to handle liquefied gases involved learning new low temperature technology. Special steels had to be developed to contain the ultra-refrigerated products. Motherwell Bridge, with its specialist metallurgy skills gained through the Hunterston nuclear power contract, and knowledge of 'cold' technology, was quickly active in the field of cryogenics. It developed and used 9 per cent nickel steel for the fabrication of refrigerated tankage and containers. Its first prototype was developed in the mid-sixties, a carbon dioxide containment vessel about 10 feet long and 4 feet in diameter, for Distillers Company Ltd. The client got quite a bargain. The small container was over-engineered to probably six times its true value as Motherwell Bridge built in many extra features, trying out its new technology.

One early challenge to be overcome in the early days once again involved the welding.

Motherwell Bridge discovered the special steel it was using became highly magnetic, making it difficult to work with.

To overcome it, new welding techniques, using A.C. rather than D.C. power supplies, had to be developed. The design team also had to take on board the effects of differing rates of metal contraction involved between outer and inner walls of containers and the effects of piping passing through them.

Having gained experience in design, construction and insulation from the prototype, Motherwell Bridge went on to build a 50 feet diameter and 50 feet high liquid oxygen tank at Carfin, Lanarkshire, for the British Oxygen Company, to be followed by a similar sized ethylene tank for BP Chemicals at Grangemouth and another oxygen tank for the North Thames Gas Board.

Then came the Glenmavis facility contract which took the company almost five years to complete in a two-phase development. It was to be one of six LNG facilities built by the company across the UK for British Gas. In 1971 and 1972 on the 130-acre Lanarkshire site Motherwell Bridge built a 20,320 tons storage tank. By the end of 1972 it was fully operational, with more than 17,000 tons of gas liquefied and stored. The second tank and liquefaction plant came into operation in March, 1975.

There were many design innovations in the double-skinned storage tanks. Both were really 'tanks within a tank.' The walls of the 151 feet diameter outer tanks were made of mild steel, capped with a dome roof, itself a major technological feat. The interior tanks were made of 9 per cent nickel steel and measured 140 feet diameter by 112 feet in height. Of an open top design, the interior tanks had an aluminium insulated flat roof suspended from the outer roof on aluminium and stainless steel hangers. Insulation between the two walls was achieved by filling the gap with perlite. In addition, the inside tanks were also enveloped in a special resilient blanket to allow for metal contraction and expansion and

had their base insulation provided by foamed glass blocks, laid to a depth of 2 feet. The storage tanks were supported on a ring beam of reinforced concrete and beneath the outer tank base plates an electrical heating system was installed to prevent the ground from freezing.

Safety was a major consideration at the Glenmavis facility. Many 'fail safe' back-up systems were introduced to handle plant processes. The storage tanks were protected from fire by a deluge system, the water coming from a high level reservoir. Nothing was left to chance. One of the outside

dangers considered was the possibility of one or both of the tanks being hit by a crashing aircraft. To cope with large-scale tank ruptures, earthern bunds were constructed round the tanks - 'dams' capable of containing up to 10 per cent more than the tanks' maximum capacity for liquid gas.

More than 20 years on Glenmavis remains a key component in Scotland's gas industry, still capable of keeping the home fires burning in an emergency. It has been calculated that it could probably supply the whole of the UK's needs for a single day, if necessary.

MAIN PICTURE: NATURAL GAS TERMINAL, GLENMAVIS. These double-wall storage tanks, 150 feet high and 150 feet in diameter can hold around 20,000 tons of liquefied natural gas at temperatures as low as minus 163 degrees C.

INSET: LNG TERMINAL. Liquefied natural gas is stored at the Isle of Grain terminal for the largest populated area of the United Kingdom, which includes London.

# CHAPTER 11

# Boldness in Adversity

Intrinsic in all heavy engineering is an element of risk. It is in the nature of the beast. Motherwell Bridge, trading across a wide range of engineering interests, is no different from its rivals in that not every contract it undertook delivered automatic profits.

Engineering markets tend to be cyclical. Investment in new equipment is often high. Some projects taken on are speculative in nature, aimed at developing new skills or opening up new markets; others are subject to price and time variables outwith company control. Yet again, others throw up additional technical problems impossible to foresee at the outset. Engineering is a trade where constant re-adjustment and amendments between the parties go on while jobs are in progress. The trick for successful companies like Motherwell Bridge is to ensure that sufficient profit streams are being generated from the over-all portfolio of activities to maintain company vigour.

Nevertheless, in business, disasters can and do happen - blowing up like unexpected tornados. In Motherwell Bridge's case it was forced into taking a £4 million loss over its involvement as a major sub-contractor in the construction of Conoco's £1 billion revolutionary tension leg platform (known as a TLP) for the Hutton oil field. There was, too, a ferocious sting in the tail.

Motherwell Bridge found itself being penalised, not because it had got anything wrong, but because, alone of the sub-contractors, it had got the technology required absolutely right.

Happening, as it did, against a background of Thatcherite Britain where world recession and an artificially high pound were allowed to drive much of Britain's manufacturing base, including UK engineering, to its knees, the TLP crisis would have floored for good many a lesser company than Motherwell Bridge. It was a time when the general economic climate, alone, was consigning many household names to oblivion in the greatest shake-out of heavy industry and manufacturing seen in the post-war years. As a non-interventionist Government looked to the City to generate the nation's wealth it was as if actually making things for our own consumption had

been declared an old-fashioned concept best left to the low-cost economies of developing nations.

Several of the mighty oaks in the forest failed to weather the economic blizzard. The first major casualty of the period was the French company, Construction Metallique de Provence (CMP) which had a strong presence in the Middle East and Africa. Its demise signalled the first of a number of company collapses within the industry.

Hardly had the shock waves from those abated than a fresh round of closures were in progress. Within years of CMP going down, it was the turn of Capper Neill, a Stock Exchange-quoted British company whose success in obtaining large contracts in extremely depressed markets had often puzzled the Motherwell Bridge management. The extent of the Capper Neill losses seemed to provide the answer. It appeared to have been under-bidding. A rescue package was launched in an attempt to save the group, only to fail as further losses came to light. The Capper Neill group folded completely.

In both instances Motherwell Bridge moved quickly to pick up some of the profitable pieces of the two giants,

**TENSION LEG PLATFORM SECTION.** Looking down from the overhead crane into the larger leg section highlighting the extent of the steelwork in these major pieces of offshore structure. The four openings are where the tension members pass through to the seabed anchors.

PREPARING FOR SHIPMENT. Two of the larger TLP leg sections ready for shipment to the north of Scotland.

# STEEL EATING BUGS DINE OUT ON MB

ONE of the oddest engineering problems ever faced by Motherwell Bridge was coping with steel-eating bugs.

In the early 1980s company metallurgists were shocked to receive complaints that pipes which the company had installed at the Isle of Grain liquid natural gas facility on the Thames had mysteriously corroded just months before the plant was to go into service. It was a strange problem, because the stainless steel piping was 12mm thick and designed to handle temperatures reaching minus 163 degrees C. It had also been thoroughly tested on installation.

The 'culprits' turned out to be micro-organisms in water which had been drawn from local supplies for pressure tests. The water, drawn from the fire hydrant system, contained a bacterium called Gallionella, which together with other micro-organisms, SRB (sulphate reducing bacteria) set up a chain reaction to create a cell which was highly partial to stressed metal at the welds. It would burrow into the metal and create much larger cavities around itself within the steel. Although the pipes had been drained out, tiny pools of the test water had been trapped at some spots, particularly near weld joints, with tiny amounts of debris. Having used drinking water for the test, no problems were expected. But the bacteria present fed on the waste material and combined, setting up a highly corrosive

chain reaction which ate through the metal in just eight months. "It took all these combined conditions to be present for the cavities to be made," said Charlie McNeilly, one of the metallurgists investigating the case. "The remedial work necessary required extensive radiographic examination to identify what were in fact very small defects."

As a result of the strange phenomenon, Motherwell Bridge had to replace or repair about 15 sections of pipe throughout the system, which it completed before the plant was scheduled to come into use. The company also introduced new drying out procedures after hydraulic pressure tests to ensure there was no repetition. About six months later at Sullom Voe, BP

faced a similar problem with Gallionella on a stainless steel pipeline running beneath a road.

Back in the mid-sixties in Abu Dhabi, another type of bug posed a problem for Motherwell Bridge when leakages from the bottom of a 500,000 barrel oil tank were discovered. Investigations showed that a micro-organism was destroying the protective coating of bitumen-type epoxy on its base. Corrosion occurred within a year of the tank being constructed.

"We never did manage to fully identify the bug," says Motherwell Bridge metallurgist David Dickie. "Its presence was deduced from circumstantial evidence. However, when we changed the type of protective coating, there were no more problems."

LNG PIPEWORK. Motherwell Bridge designed, supplied and installed stainless steel pipework at the British Gas, Isle of Grain liquid natural gas facility.

with mixed success. In the case of CMP the barrier proved not to be one of language but one of encountering a perhaps not unnatural Gallic preference for their businesses to be French-owned. Even so, acquisitions from CMP and Capper Neill were made by Motherwell Bridge at relatively modest cost and gave instant results at a time when they were very much needed. Acquisitions from CMP included a heat exchanger company with links to the French nuclear industry and from Capper Neill the Group gained several companies including CNC, a control systems company which later became Motherwell Control Systems. Another profitable acquisition - traded very successfully for several years before being sold on - was UDEC, a company which handled refrigeration plant.

In common with the rest of the industry, the main problem for Motherwell Bridge in the early 1980s was the severe lack of work for its fabrication workshops. Often the company found itself having to retrench. Those contractions brought with them a number of write-offs. However, in what was an extremely difficult trading period for everyone, the Group remained, albeit in some years marginally, in profit - a feat not always emulated by its competitors who did not have profit streams available from a prosperous travel wing, a growing information systems business and a busy spell producing under licence plant for the soon to be acquired Dano, the world leader in composting and waste reduction technology (See separate panel, page 162). There was no denying it, though; the early 1980s were pretty hard going.

That Motherwell Bridge not only survived the TLP saga but went on, through a mixture of new trading and bold acquisitions, to return the company to full profitability by the end of the decade (substantially up on the lean years) speaks volumes for the financial robustness of the company, and the tough-mindedness of its management team. Throughout it all they kept their nerve.

Very sensibly, management adopted a strategy, when it became possible, of first ring-fencing the TLP venture so that its enormous drain on executive time did not divert the company's attention from its other, profitable activities. Then in the middle of all its difficulties, and still with no clear idea what the final outcome of the TLP case would be, Motherwell Bridge undertook what was a very bold step indeed - it traded itself out of trouble through growth by major acquisition.

John Crawford and John Lumsden recommended to the Holdings Board that the company buy the prosperous JGB Group in the north east of Scotland.

Run by two brothers, Bill and Hamish Barrack, the JGB Group was in property, industrial warehousing which it had built itself, and transport services. It also held a lucrative Mercedes Benz dealership and was a major servicer of the rigs, including North Sea catering. Most important of all, it gave Motherwell Bridge the entree it sought into oil field supplies, kick-starting the Group's ambitions to further expand its distribution side.

"It was a brave move, but the right one", says John Lumsden. "We saw that if we didn't make that acquisition we weren't going to see a growth ahead. Acquiring JGB gave us the ability to project increasing profits forward and gave the banks and others greater confidence in our future prospects. That might not have been the case if we had just sat tight and worried about when we would recover our own money. We realised that if we could project a growing profit stream beyond TLP then we would give people confidence in our future".

In a cleverly constructed deal, Motherwell Bridge bought JGB for £5 million on deferred terms, a move that inspired and bolstered investor confidence, the life's blood of any business. It was a pivotal deal of the 1980s. It gave the Group an added dimension and laid down much more solidly than ever before the pattern of diversification it wished to establish for the future, reducing its dependence on 'boom and bust' capital spending cycles which were a regular feature of its traditional markets.

Motherwell Bridge had emerged from the buoyant 1970s looking to three principal areas to provide it with steady profits generation on top of its normal range of activities: distribution, engineering services and a fledgling control systems technology division (prior to TLP, it had just moved into the field by purchasing a 50 per cent stake in a family business in Kansas which provided automated material handling systems to the grain industry).

However, just as that quest embracing new technology was beginning, Motherwell Bridge in the early 1980s found its attentions focused for all the wrong reasons on Conoco's TLP, a 'world first' in engineering technology. Although not strictly needed for Hutton, which was in only 485 feet of water and could have been serviced by a

**TLP SECTION LOAD OUT.** The first of the larger leg section components for the tension leg platform being loaded onto the barge at the company's Western Harbour, Leith offshore facility. With the unit in place the multi-wheeled bogies and tractor can be seen on the right, being removed.

normal fixed platform, the TLP was designed by Conoco engineers as the forerunner of a new breed of floating tension leg platforms required for deep sea oil extraction. Unlike conventional platforms, which sit on the sea bed, the TLP was a semi-submersible structure moored vertically to the bottom by tubular steel tethers. Buoyancy from its partially submerged hull created the upward force needed to hold its legs under permanent tension in all weather conditions - much in the way a buoy anchored partially below the water surface strains against its mooring rope.

The plan was to make the TLP in two halves, 'mate' them at a sheltered deep water site in the Moray Firth, then tow out the completed platform to the Hutton field 90 miles north-east of the Shetland Isles. As one of the two main sub-contractors to Highland Fabricators, Motherwell Bridge was signed up to fabricate two of the platform's corner columns, C1 and C2, in July, 1981, and work began in September. They were massive constructions. In total, the columns weighed more than 3,700 tons, and were 55 feet in diameter. Because of their size they were built in a series of sections ranging in height from 26 feet to 39 feet.

Given the Hunterston experience, which had seen Motherwell Bridge lay down as policy that it would no longer take on major contracts in pioneering engineering, the decision to get involved with the TLP project seemed to

flout that directive. However, Motherwell Bridge could be forgiven for taking it on. The TLP was being flagged up by Conoco not as pioneering technology, but as a new design making use of well tested engineering procedures. Motherwell Bridge's sector of the work, which involved heavy reliance on metallurgy know-how and top quality welding (in which it was a UK leader), lay at the very core of its own fabrication expertise so the company did not anticipate any major technical problems beyond the normal challenges thrown up in any large-scale engineering endeavour.

What the Group had not bargained for, however, was the composition of the steel being provided by the client. After running its own metallurgical tests, Motherwell Bridge very quickly came to the conclusion that to achieve the standard of welding being sought, and to avoid cracking of the welds, plates would require to be pre-heated to temperatures of between 50 and 100 degrees C. It was a revelation greeted with much incredulity by Highland Fabricators. There had been no mention in the Conoco specifications of pre-heating. Motherwell Bridge, however, stuck to its guns. Alone of the trio of contractors, it devised a system of pre-heating sections the men were working on by building metal box units - known as 'cans' - around them.

For welding, the standards being insisted upon were extremely high, and barely capable of being replicated outside laboratory conditions. Even tack welds - a temporary procedure to hold plates together for ease of manoeuvrability - at the insistence of the inspectors had to be inserted at preset distances and in specified numbers.

Project manager Stewart Paterson vividly recalls journey after journey to Pitlochry - a halfway point between the Highlands and Motherwell Bridge - for technical meetings with Highland Fabricators and others to thrash out details on what welding procedures could be used and when, and the sense of frustration at the obstacles being encountered.

What Motherwell Bridge did not realise, however, is that even at fairly early stages of the contract (early 1982) the company was already an embarrassment. Mitsui and Highland Fabricators were both experiencing welding difficulties. In fact, the Japanese

company had to gouge out something like seven miles of welding and reweld using pre-heating. Highland Fabricators had just discovered the first cracks in their welding and were being forced to do the same.

In the complex web of constantly revised specifications, if all three parties, Highland Fabricators, Mitsui and Motherwell Bridge, had experienced the same problems in welding, a united front could have been presented to Conoco, requiring the multi-national to meet the heavy additional costs on what had started out as a tightly priced contract. They would have had an extremely strong claim, as would Conoco from its own insurers.

It became public knowledge in September, 1982, that welding cracks had been found in the hull of the TLP on work carried out by Highland Fabricators. With no hope of the overall contract meeting its deadlines, Conoco accepted it was going to miss its weather "window" and

**TANK GAUGES AT CORYTON REFINERY.** Motherwell Bridge designs, manufactures, installs and maintains high accuracy tank gauging systems for the oil and petrochemical industries worldwide. Two hundred high accuracy servo tank gauges were installed at BP's Coryton Refinery in Essex.

**OFFSHORE SERVICES.** Transport services for the offshore market was one field in which the company's Aberdeen operations were involved.

rescheduled completion dates for 1984. However, as the contract continued, Motherwell Bridge, still not receiving cash for work done, rather than dig itself into an even deeper financial morass, agreed to hand over its corner columns, C1 and C2, to Highland Fabricators for completion.

The hand-over was achieved not without considerable tensions. A contract that for Motherwell Bridge had started out at £5 million and had spiralled to £19-20 million had both sides reviewing their options.

For two years Motherwell Bridge prepared for a legal arbitration. It lodged a claim for £26 million, of which £12 million was for extra work, against Highland Fabricators. HiFab, in turn, lodged a counter-claim of more than £8 million for finishing off the C1 and C2 platform columns. Some inkling of the case's complexity can be garnered from the fact that more than seven tons of documents were amassed by Motherwell Bridge in support of its claim.

Frustratingly for Motherwell Bridge, the arbitration was abandoned without a single witness being called. For all its ramifications, Motherwell Bridge's case largely hinged on one crucial question: had Highland Fabricators breached the terms of its contract by failing to pass on cash it had received from Conoco for pre-heating carried out by the sub-contractors? At the conclusion of the marathon opening of the case, the short answer to that question from the arbiter was No. Motherwell Bridge's contract was with

Highland Fabricators, not Conoco.

The central plank of Motherwell Bridge's argument - that Highland Fabricators had been paid twice for the same work - had been seriously compromised.

The huge expense of calling witnesses was unlikely to alter greatly that finding. Faced with the prospect of a further year in court, and with no certainty of winning an arbitration which was obviously going to be decided on tight legal grounds, rather than technical ones, Motherwell Bridge withdrew. Both parties bore their own legal costs.

For the company, the most damaging aspect of the case was not monetary. It was the way it had sucked senior personnel into its vortex. Companies only prosper by looking forward; the TLP venture had many senior executives forced constantly to look backwards until the company eventually was able to ring fence it, allowing management to concentrate fully on more normal activities. Elsewhere, there were other challenges to be met. Fabrication work was going through one of its periodic downturns, with oil companies putting the squeeze on prices in an overcrowded market.

Motherwell Bridge, refusing to enter into cut-throat bidding, was forced to retrench. It brought fabrication back to Motherwell from Uphall to combat spiralling costs as a temporary measure.

Since the 1960s Motherwell Bridge had been striving, with mixed success, to develop alternative sources of trade in engineering-related sectors which would generate steady profits outside of the 'stop-go' cycles of capital projects. In the 1980s that goal became more sharply defined than ever before: acquisition; assimilation of the sector it wished to be in (in this case a greater range of oil field supplies); steady growth and nurturing of the other assets while taking good annual profits; and the disposal of those assets at the right time for handsome returns.

The decade's pivotal purchase of the JGB Group proved a textbook example. Acquired for £5 million, the company traded along giving a good return on the investment. After some three or four years, when the property market picked up, Motherwell Bridge sold its North of Scotland property portfolio for £4 million. That was to be followed, in 1994, by the sale of the Mercedes dealership, which Motherwell Bridge had continued to grow, for £4.5 million. The company had more than recovered its original investment, while still retaining JGB's transport and oil field services, the sector which fitted neatly into its mainstream activities.

If the purchase of JGB was the key acquisition of the 1980s, equally it could be said that the watershed year of that decade for the company was 1986. It was the year the Group introduced probably its most major reorganisation in 20 years and completed the laying of the foundations for the Divisional structures which, by and large, continue to pertain today.

In the years prior to 1986 there had been a fair amount of reorganisation within the Group, much of it - it has to be said - introduced in response to the rapidly altering trading circumstances in which Motherwell Bridge found itself; the changes had tended to be reactive rather than pro-active. In what was an extremely severe depression, the Motherwell Bridge Board was prepared to look far and wide at potential new profit sources, no matter how unlikely. At one juncture, when fabrication was at its lowest ebb, the Board gave serious consideration to selling off a large slice of its head office site for use as a shopping development. That it didn't happen was solely due to local planning restrictions.

The internal company restructuring which occurred in 1986, however, was of a different order to what had gone before. Triggered, in part, by a disastrous slump in oil prices which saw the oil companies pull back on fabrication and other work, it was in essence the last piece of the jigsaw aimed at making Motherwell Bridge

less dependent upon oil-related industry for its existence. One could hardly fault the Group's management in such an ambition: in the late 1970s the company had found itself being financially clobbered by a spectacular OPEC-inspired oil price hike; now, having spent virtually the whole of the 1980s trading under the lash of exceptionally strong Sterling against the oil currency, the US dollar (the pound was valued at around 2 dollars 40), Motherwell Bridge was again being financially penalised - this time by an oil price slump. In its most major trading arena, it didn't seem to matter much which way the market went - it still lost out.

Thus the Group had its sights very much set on the future, managing a portfolio of interests outside the sphere of the oil industry which offered a steady profit stream.

In the shake-up it established a new management team of executives to handle the Divisions within a better framework and reporting system - one which would maximise efficient and cost-effective control and development of Group assets. It was an expensive programme of change, but it wasn't long before the benefits began filtering through. By 1988 the improvements had been translated into solid financial gains.

Despite a decade for much of which traditional sectors had failed to generate the volumes of work the company was looking for, only 'bottoming out' in 1988-89, Motherwell Bridge emerged from the decade stronger and more vigorous than ever.

It had money in its pocket. A judicious mix of rationalisation, re-organisation and occasional sales of mature assets saw it make up lost ground to return profits of £4.1 million in the late 1980s which were considerably up on the lean years. The mid-1980s had seen it win lucrative new work in Africa, first in Nigeria constructing a food processing plant, then in Ghana refurbishing the country's large Italian-built refinery (the first of four phases of refurbishments carried out). It had not allowed a multi-million pound financial thunderbolt to deflect it from its business goals and its appetite for acquisition, expansion and diversification in chosen fields remained undiminished. In short, Motherwell Bridge had taken it on the chin and still prospered. It was with considerable confidence that the company prepared to enter the final decade of the 20th century - and a centenary of trading.

# GREEN GLORY DAYS RETURN

ONE of the success stories of the 1980s for Motherwell Bridge was its involvement with Dano, the world's best-known company in refuse composting. Motherwell Bridge in 1980 began building environmentally friendly Dano plants under licence for municipal authorities in Britain - and by 1986 owned the famous company lock, stock and barrel. It was a considerable coup. Dano enjoys international branding for its name on a level with Hoover. With some 200 Dano plants constructed around the world, at its peak it had a phenomenally high slice of the world composting market amounting to around 25 per cent.

Dano's big attraction is that its system is environmentally friendly, versatile and simple to run. With a possible plant life of anything up to 30 years and beyond, its special giant rotary drums which are the key feature of its plants, can be used either to produce two grades of stable landfill from mixed waste - or, in conjunction with other processes, an excellent natural compost for agricultural use.

Founded at the turn of the century in Copenhagen, Denmark, Dano, a firm of engineers and boilermakers, revolutionised waste management in 1935 by developing and building the world's first mechanised plant for the treatment and composting of household rubbish. It went on to worldwide success before being

bought over in 1972 by a consortium of Swiss bankers. Relocated to Glarus, Switzerland, and under the direction of Victor Stahlschmidt, it began permitting plant to be built under licence in certain territories.

Motherwell Bridge's involvement with the company began when it bought over Simsons of Edinburgh, which held a Dano marketing licenseeship for the UK and was looking for a partner to develop the British market. At that time the actual manufacturing licence for the U.K. was held by an English company, General Engineering. But when the company went into liquidation, Motherwell Bridge executives moved quickly to acquire the rights from the Official Receiver. The three-pronged deal was an ideal match. Motherwell Bridge, with its proven track record in building incinerators, had a wide knowledge of the waste management field, and was a tailor-made candidate to take over Dano manufacturing rights. In Simsons, it had acquired a

relatively young company too small to handle the heavy financial investment needed to open up the market. By taking over the company, and bringing its managing director Sandy Simson into an executive role within Motherwell Bridge, the Group was 'hitting the deck running' with a brand new line of product.

In 1980, Motherwell Bridge built its first Dano plant for North Manchester to produce good quality landfill. The £6 million plant, formally opened in October, 1981, was followed in quick succession by orders for three more £6 million plants for the Greater Manchester area. Like the first, all were turnkey projects. The new plants were sited at Manchester South, Stockport and Salford and were followed in short order by contracts to build two more plants in Wales, where the company had constructed a Dano plant in 1980. One was sited in Snowdonia National Park. In that ecologically sensitive area, Dano was the only acceptable

MUNICIPAL WASTE TREATMENT. Twin Dano drums at Manchester handle some 600 tons of municipal waste per day. The drums measure 12 feet in diameter and are 80 feet in length. They have a capacity of over 18 tons per hour and rotate at between 1.2 and 3.6 revolutions per minute.

MAIN PICTURE: Egyptian Composting Plant. The composting plant handles some 100 tons of municipal waste per day. The drum measures approximately 10 feet in diameter, is 36 feet in length and rotates at ten revolutions per minute.

INSET: TRANSFER STATION Following Dano treatment, the inert and organic fractions which have been separated as part of the process are loaded into separate containers for transport by rail to a landfill site.

waste system to be permitted inside the park's environs.

Between 1984 and 1986 in Egypt, Motherwell Bridge constructed three more Dano plants, worth between £3 million and £4 million each, at Alexandria, Giza and Cairo through a World Bank backed aid project. The plants were an instantly successful addition to the Egyptian infrastructure. With their much higher levels of bio-degradable material in household rubbish, large quantities could be recycled as compost which, to this day, remains in high demand from Egyptian farmers, defraying plant running costs by a very acceptable margin.

Since acquiring Dano, Motherwell Bridge has re-organised and increased the number of foreign licenseeships. It is now preparing to market worldwide a revolutionary anaerobic process for extracting renewable energy at Dano plants.

Despite their relative simplicity in engineering terms, Dano plants are surprisingly versatile. Their giant revolving drums, which each can handle up to 300 tons of material a day, reducing waste volume by a factor of three to one, allow a 'build on' factor for several different functions. The latest application for Dano drums, developed over two years by Motherwell Bridge with part-funding from Britain's Trade and Industry Department, is in the field of energy retrieval, based on anaerobic digestion of the 'fine' material from the Dano process.

At their most basic level as a pre-treatment for landfill, the drums pulverise and homogenise waste, producing 'heavy' and 'light' landfill material. But the process also helps bio-degradable waste quickly rid itself of much more of its methane gas content than other methods. Now Motherwell Bridge, working with the Waste Management Division of Thames Water, has spent two years developing processes to very efficiently extract the methane gas as a source of renewable energy, converting it into electricity. It will help local authorities meet targets of recycling 25 per cent of household waste by the year 2000.

# Reaping the Rewards of Success

Anew millennium approaches. Few of us can hazard a guess at the technological wonders that even its first century will hold. In much less than a hundred years, no more than a blink of time's eye, the world moved from the first stuttering flight of the Wright brothers' Kitty Hawk above a Missouri field to landing a man on the moon. The revolution in other areas of engineering and physics has been no less spectacular. Mankind's technology has come so far and so fast that it is impossible to predict where the next pioneering advance will come from, or how its applications will trickle down into national infrastructures and our everyday lives. It was the space race which gave us the non-stick frying pan.

Fostered and sustained by the quantum leaps taking place in computerisation, itself probably as important an invention as the wheel, the ingenuity of the human race will continue to flower in new and unexpected ways. Of one thing, though, we may be reasonably confident. Motherwell Bridge will be in the thick of it.

If 100 years of trading has revealed anything about the company, it is that it has the corporate skills, vision and adaptability not just to survive but to prosper. It is a problem-solving company. It also enters the run-up to the millennium with a strong corporate business team headed up by chief executive John Lumsden. At 56, he has a long track record with Motherwell Bridge, having joined the company as management accountant in 1962, the same year as he qualified as a Chartered Accountant, and remained with it ever since. He was appointed financial director of the main trading company of the Group in 1974, joined the Group Management Board two years later, and the Board of the parent company, Motherwell Bridge Holdings Ltd., in 1980. He was appointed Group chief executive in January, 1989. His other business interests include being a member of the Scottish Industrial Development Advisory Board, a director of Lanarkshire Development Agency and a member of the Scottish Exports Forum. A former member of the Council of the Scottish Confederation of British Industry (1985 - 1990), he was awarded a C.B.E. for his services to Scottish industry in 1997.

A quietly authoritative man, Lumsden's 35 years with Motherwell Bridge have given him an in-depth knowledge of his markets - highly important in an industry where it can be just as important to know what fields to stay out of, as it is to develop new trading opportunities. Experience counts. But then collectively the Group's corporate team bring to bear great business experience and marketing sophistication in equipping Motherwell Bridge with the span of trading skills it will need in the years ahead.

At the outset of this company history, one question was posed: why has Motherwell Bridge succeeded while around it so many famous names disappeared? We are now a lot nearer to the answer. If at times the company's development has read like the Perils of Pauline, it is just because that was the way it was. Engineering, particularly heavy engineering, is a tough game. Its trading margins, compared to other types of businesses, are fairly small, running around the 5 per cent level. Capital outlays are high and there isn't much room for error in bidding contracts. Financial returns can be 'lumpy' because often the work is a one-off multi-million-pound major capital project or locked into the cyclical nature of the petrochemical industries.

For probably the last 40 years out of the first 100 Motherwell Bridge has been on a quest to solve the trading conundrum of cyclical business, widening out its spectrum of activities and skills in search of a stable profits growth pattern. In the past, achieving balance and the correct 'mix' has not always been possible because of a variety of factors, but the constant striving for it has eventually gained the company its just reward.

In the 1990s all the best elements tried and tested and developed from the 1950s onwards have been refashioned into a much more tightly focused package of trading interests than ever before. Motherwell Bridge today is involved in a twin track strategy of controlled diversification and building on its existing strengths. Through a combination of organic growth and growth by selective acquisition, the company is much less a hostage to fortune of cyclical trends than at any time in its history.

THOR. Thermal hydraulic hot pool test rig (THOR) - a simulator for the flow of liquids of any nature - within the UKAEA's facility at Risley, near Warrington.

Diversification coupled with healthy reserves (one of the strongest features of the company down the decades) has allowed it to restructure and invest internally, ironing out most of the bumps in its profitability and equipping itself for the future. The company looks to four separate Divisions to provide its profits - manufacturing, engineering services, information systems and distribution.

All are being structured for growth in niche markets which offer steady, long-term business. Being fields which are largely knowledge and technology-led, rather than capital intensive, the scope for expansion is considerable.

It was at the beginning of the 1990s that Motherwell Bridge began the task of re-organising itself into its new Divisional structure. The Divisions report directly to the company's 10-strong Group Management Board. Comprising the five directors of the main Holdings Board, the four executives heading up the Divisions, and the finance director, it is responsible for all Group trading activities. Above it, the smaller Holdings Board acts as a clearing house, concerning itself principally with acquisitions, investments and corporate policy. With a hard core of around thirty main subsidiary companies in its four Divisions, Motherwell Bridge is a very different beast from the company set up by the League of Gentlemen in the drawing room of Alexander Clark King's home in Motherwell in 1898.

Today a radically restructured Manufacturing Division, under the control of former Lanarkshire Development Agency boss Archie Bethel, handles high quality metal forming, welding, precision machining and equipment manufacture. Very much founded in Motherwell Bridge's traditional and specialist engineering skills, the Holdings Group in 1994 broadened the range of the Division's markets by acquiring Clayton Son & Co. (Holdings) plc, a world-famous engineering group headquartered in Leeds. To date, at £3.4 million, it has been Motherwell Bridge's single largest acquisition of the decade - and

STORAGE SYSTEM. Hydrochloric acid and sodium hydroxide storage tanks, pumps and associated pipework were designed, constructed and tested for Ciba Geigy in Paisley.

through sympathetic restructuring and selective assets sales the Group has already recouped its purchase price twice over, without compromising the integrity of its engineering strengths. The funds realised have been reinvested in modernised plant and equipment.

Actually slightly longer established than Motherwell Bridge, Claytons had also gone down the acquisition trail, diversifying from its original base of constructing domestic and industrial gas holders in search of stable profitability. It had bought over a number of 'old name' engineering companies such as Fielding & Platt, Chester Hydraulics and John Shaw, of Manchester, pulling them together to form a highly specialist hydraulic press group. For Motherwell Bridge the big attraction was that Claytons had gone down a different route from themselves, opening up completely new markets in the aluminium and automotive industries.

Through Claytons, Motherwell Bridge has established a foothold in the US automobile industry, producing presses used to make car radiators. The English subsidiary also developed a special deep drawn press which, from a single blank metal plate, can extrude a "one-piece" compressed gas cylinder for use in vehicles - a truly amazing technological feat of mechanical engineering. Motherwell Bridge will also receive a spin-off in supplying replacement seals and parts.

The take-over of Claytons was a most amicable acquisition. Motherwell Bridge had known the company for 25 years, having in 1973 bought a 50 per cent stake in an Australian subsidiary of theirs which was in structural steel and tank building, but which lacked the expertise needed to construct large diameter tankage. That long and friendly relationship resulted in a fine 'marriage' of interests which saw Motherwell Bridge achieve a Manufacturing Division with new in-house specialist skills and a batch of important new markets. Claytons being a listed company, and Motherwell Bridge a private one, it had to buy the English group off the Stock Exchange.

The Engineering Services Division, within the U.K., is in the charge of Alan Murphy. It handles everything from turnkey projects to site and plant maintenance in the petrochemical, gas, pharmaceutical, environmental and electronics industries. The oil industry in the U.K., while no longer involved in large tankage and refinery expansions, still provides a very steady work stream from Motherwell Bridge's maintenance contracts for places like Sullom Voe

RADIATOR CORE PRESS. A press produced at the company's Leeds facility for the manufacture of aluminium radiator cores.

and Flotta, and refineries at Humberside, Grangemouth and Southampton.

More recently the Division has been active in electronics plant, providing high purity pipework for the semi-conductor industry in Scotland. Abroad, the trend has been to seek out selective contracts which have an 'added value' dimension, bringing additional work to the company's engineering and fabrication activities.

The diversification of the Division has been substantial. In construction, the steel, cement and glass industries are the source of a strong order book. Recent contracts gained include a £7.5 million order for a new cement plant at Rugby, upon which work will begin next year. Other multi-million pound contracts include the dismantling of part of a steelworks in Switzerland for shipment to Indonesia and the installation of a pulverised fuel injection plant at Port Talbot.

At the other end of the spectrum, the Division also handles installations of a different kind - the moving of delicate hardware into factories for electronics industry leaders such as NEC, Motorola, Siemens and Digital. Through Semicon Installations of East Kilbride, which it set up three years ago, Motherwell Bridge recently completed a transfer of £300 million worth of new equipment into an electronics plant without incurring a single scratch. In what is a highly specialist 'removal service' the company employs hi-tech methods. It uses dinnerplate sized hovercraft - known as air glide skates - to position hardware in premises. In a rapidly growing market, Semicon's expertise is now being sought out by US companies setting up electronics plant in Europe.

Another growth market for the Division is high purity specialist pipework. Once largely the preserve of the medical field, the need for small bore orbitally welded stainless steel pipework produced in sterile conditions is now growing rapidly in the semi-conductor and gases industries. With four mobile clean rooms (complete with airlocks and estimated to be one hundred times more sterile than hospital operating theatres) and plans for a static clean room to be custom-built at company headquarters, Motherwell Bridge is recognised as the UK leader in the field.

It has recently entered into a business alliance with British Oxygen Company to manufacture all gas separation units for BOC plants within Europe, a multi-million pounds agreement which the company hopes to see extended worldwide.

The Division is also becoming more active in the field of nuclear plant decommissioning.

The Information Systems Division, one of the big current growth areas, under the control of Bob Johnson, provides and installs highly sophisticated information and industrial computerised control systems.
For the nuclear industry it has created systems for tracking and storage of treated nuclear waste.
Elsewhere, for a variety of industries, it has designed and installed custom-built systems used to route and monitor every stage of plant production processes. The Division has its own software house which designs immensely versatile systems to control everything from plant input, tracking of product through the plant to final distribution and transport management. Fairly typical of the systems the electronics division designs are cost-effective resource management systems for, say, a board mill whose clients ask for materials in a variety of different sizes, or working out 'best practice' container loading and the most economical run for a New Zealand company shipping goods round Asia.

The Division is not above applying its know-how to its own operations. A radical overhaul of its internal communications and the pooling of shared resources and market information between the various subsidiaries saw a dramatic 50 per cent rise in the Information Systems Division's profitability in 1996. The Division also has set its sights firmly on establishing new trade links in China and the Pacific Rim nations. With a base already solidly established in Australia and New Zealand, selling company products and expertise, the Division also has a presence in Beijing and recently complemented that foothold by opening new offices in both Taiwan and Hong Kong. Closer to home, it is targeting the pharmaceutical market with its specialist systems.

The evolvement of the Information Systems Division is interesting in that it is a fairly typical example of the way Motherwell Bridge sets about entering any new field of technology or engineering. Back in the late 1970s the U.K. Government's Department of Trade and Industry ran a promotion where they gave away a micro-processor, publicising the importance of the computer chip. One landed on the desk of John Crawford, who immediately realised that here was an industrial tool of great significance. In his hand he held a device which could store information, produce codes, translate measurements and temperatures into alternative measurements and even organise traffic sequences.

"I didn't fully understand how it worked, but I appreciated its immense power," he says. "I realised there and then that as a company we had to get in with the chip - and that we were really quite late in getting into electronics".

Motherwell Bridge immediately began casting around for an entree into electronic technology. Within months, in 1978, it bought the U.K. subsidiary of an Australian company, Inflo Belt Weighers, which, in Crawford's words, was "all chips and clever electronics," making a device which electronically weighed the materials travelling along conveyor belts. It was not an especially large acquisition, but it was an extremely significant one. For Motherwell Bridge it was a start in electronics, learning the new technology involved and networking in a new industry. The U.K. arm of Inflo Belt Weighers - eventually to be sold to its own management in a MBO some five years ago after 14 years' profitable trading - was the direct stepping stone to Motherwell Bridge's creation of its own Information Systems Division.

**PICTURE, NEXT PAGE: INFORMATION TECHNOLOGY.**
The company's Information Systems Division uses best-in-class computer software and hardware to provide information systems and control solutions for the process industries.

# IMPORTANT ROLE OF NON-EXECUTIVE DIRECTORS

THE appointment of non-executive directors to the Board of Motherwell Bridge has always been an important feature of the Group. In the early years they were drawn from the original shareholders. Certainly, the original board of A.R. Miller, John Marshall and Robert Park were probably all non-executives as each had their own businesses to look after.

The first independent non-executive director was John Westall Pearson, the London-based chairman and managing director of British Oil and Cake Mills, who was appointed to the board in 1923 at the instigation of T.R. Miller, and remained a director until his death in April, 1959. The second Ronald Miller brought to the Board men of the calibre of Sir Arnold Lindley, ex-chairman of G.E.C., and Alan Robertson and Robin Adam, both former BP directors. Another top executive, Cameron McLatchie, chairman and chief executive of British Polythene Industries plc served on the Board for four years until May, 1997.

The present non-executive representation is as strong as ever: Duncan MacLeod, ex-partner of (as it then was) Ernst & Whinney, of Glasgow, who as audit partner had been responsible for the company audit for many years; Sir Gordon Manzie, former chief executive of the Property Services Agency, Sandy Findlay, chairman of Hewden Stuart plc, and the most recent appointment - Duncan Whyte, Multi Utility director of Scottish Power. The present chairman, Ian Preston, formerly head of Scottish Power, is the Group's first non-executive chairman since the days of John Alston.

wnership of this company in 1981 led Motherwell Bridge to taking a 50 per cent interest in an American mid-western electronics company, Control Systems Inc., of Kansas. A family business run by Jim Shirley, it devised automated handling systems for the grain industry in America's wheat belt. With the new capital, it considerably expanded its operations, automating systems for major grain terminals across the USA. It was a hugely successful investment for Motherwell Bridge, which encouraged the company to get into new markets, adapting systems for many other fields, including the railroad and oil industries, and returned excellent dividends for the company.
In 1994 Motherwell Bridge sold its holding back to the family for 17 million dollars, a first-class return on an original investment of one million dollars. By that time, however, Motherwell Bridge had very successfully grown the Information Systems Division through a mixture of expansion and acquisition.

With one of the Division's target markets being China, the company in the mid-1990s invested in a Perth, Australia, company, which already had experience of working in the republic. That investment paid off handsomely, with its technology teams winning an £8 million contract for the control and automation of a conveyer system at a steelworks at Baoshan some

**BELOW: ROTTERDAM BRIDGE.** A pedestrian and bicycle bridge over the Ringvaartplas in Rotterdam supplied and erected by the company's Dutch operation.

12 miles from Shanghai. It will pave the way for further contracts as the most populous nation on earth continues its breathtakingly rapid surge forward to modernise its industrial base and infrastructures.

The growth of the Information Systems Division is, in microcosm, very much the way Motherwell Bridge has evolved: it prospects the field it wants to enter, dips a toe in the water, then as it acquires knowledge, expands further into it. When it has fully absorbed the new skills, it moves on to bigger and better things in the same field - either by licenseeships, joint ventures or direct acquisition.

As fate would have it, Motherwell Bridge was to find itself back in Kansas City as owners of another information systems company, CIMDEC run by a former CSI executive Roger Resley. Again there was an

**BELOW: COMPUTERISED MANUFACTURING.** The company supplied a complete turnkey solution for a computerised manufacturing execution system for Glaxo Wellcome UK.

The system allows for complete operator guidance in a paperless environment, managing critical documentation and maintaining compliance in a heavily regulated pharmaceutical environment.

Using the latest technology, the system is integrated with manufacturing planning, maximising the benefit of management information.

ABOVE: CLYDESIDE FABRICATION. Prefabrication of cold boxes for a British Oxygen Company air separation plant in Austria.

RIGHT: STAINLESS STEEL PIPEWORK. The company installed stainless steel pipework and vessels at Roche Products' facility in Dalry, Ayrshire.

BOTTOM RIGHT: AIR WINCHES. Motherwell Bridge is the leading supplier of air winches to the oil and gas industry on and offshore and also operates the largest rental service to rigs, platforms and semi submersible vessels operating offshore.

Antipodean connection: Cimdec was a wholly owned subsidiary of a New Zealand group which Motherwell Bridge bought over bringing Roger once more into the Motherwell Bridge fold.

Today, despite its late start in electronics, Motherwell Bridge has built up an Information Systems Division which encompasses both maturity and innovation. In the last few years it has further strengthened its technology base by selective acquisitions which are benefiting it in the water, energy, transportation and nuclear industries.

The Distribution Division, under the control of Malcolm Phillips, is another important growth area for the company. The Division featured in the single greatest profit-taking in company history: the sell-off in 1996 of its business travel 'empire', Portman Travel. Motherwell Bridge sold the travel group for the sort of profit which would have most corporate executives gnawing at the carpet in envy. The sale realised £21.4 million - on an original investment of £5,000 back in 1967.

(See full panel story).

Not that the remainder of the Distribution Division has been laggard in its achievements. In 1996 it doubled its profits from its other interests, which today lie principally in supplying and servicing a wide variety of North Sea and other industries with compressors, welding consumables, equipment and replacement parts.

The Division operates the biggest distribution service of its kind in Scotland and the North of England. Further business purchases have given it additional outlets in Fife and the North of England. The Division is now extending operations southwards, having acquired a company specialising in the sale and servicing of compressors and spare parts from three outlets in the South of England.

**INSET RIGHT: VOID PROPERTY PROTECTION.** Security windows and doors are fitted to property being refurbished.

**BELOW:** Motherwell Bridge supplied and installed six Ingersoll Rand SSR MM110 compressors on the Forth Railway Bridge in Scotland. This world famous bridge crosses the Firth of Forth and is the main east coast rail crossing out of Edinburgh for trains destined for Dundee and Aberdeen. The compressors are strategically positioned across the length of the bridge to provide compressed air for the ongoing maintenance of the structure.

The Distribution Division has also opened up an unusual growth market, renting out protective steel shuttering and security doors for empty property. Having opened up excellent business in Scotland, it is gearing up to market the specialist service across Britain and overseas. There is considerable scope for expansion and it is expected to be a long-term winner for the Group.

Down the years Motherwell Bridge has looked to the Distribution Division to contribute substantially to Group profitability, particularly in the slack periods of major heavy engineering capital investment. Its task has always been to seek out avenues of business capable of sustaining a steady flow of income, independent of cyclical trends.

By its nature, the Distribution Division is constantly on the look-out for good ideas in the services sector which, but for an injection of capital or additional marketing expertise, might otherwise wither on the vine. In its search for new opportunities across an international stage it is very much in the entrepreneurial mould.

# £21 MILLION TRAVEL EMPIRE BOUGHT FOR £5,000

IN every company legends build up around pivotal business deals. The purchase by Motherwell Bridge of the London travel agency, Portman Travel Ltd., for £5,000 and its sale nearly 30 years later for a staggering £21.4 million has attracted its own fair share of mystique. Within Motherwell Bridge most people will tell you with relish how in April, 1967, two executives, director Jock Anderson and assistant company secretary Iain Macleod, walked into Portman's London office to pick up a couple of flight tickets. Unable to have them issued because Portman's credit rating had been suspended, 'Tanky' Anderson pulled out his cheque book and there and then on the spur of the moment bought the company, debts and all - then told it to get on with arranging the flight tickets.

Like all such tales there is more than a kernel of truth in it. But the real story of Portman Travel's acquisition was slightly more prosaic, although it most certainly was a whirlwind deal, being accomplished in a single day. However, the groundwork had been partially laid beforehand.

Portman Travel was the London offshoot of Alghanim Travel Agency, which handled business travel in the Middle East. Its founder wanted to pull out of the British end of the operation because it was losing money. Learning of the company's proposal to divest itself of its U.K. office, Portman's London manager, Norman Flack, contacted Anderson, whom he knew well as a regular client, to see if he would consider a purchase. An early sale was vital. If there was any hiatus in trading the result would be a loss of goodwill and jobs.

Because of his Mothercat role in the Lebanon, Anderson was very familiar with Alghanims and its executives, who had close links to Mothercat's joint venture partner, Emile Bustani. In addition, over the previous 20 years he and Motherwell Bridge overseas personnel had made regular use of its services. With an eye for a bargain, Anderson was struck by several factors: business travel was a growth market and there was scope for Motherwell Bridge to handle all its own travel business through the company; it had a plum office location in Portman Square, one of London's most elegant and sought after business areas. Lastly, it had in Norman Flack a manager of exceptionally high calibre. Indeed, as they entered into negotiations, both 'Tanky' and Macleod had privately agreed beforehand: no Norman, no deal.

Anderson programmed the purchase of Portman Travel over a single day before he and Macleod flew off to Africa. It began with meetings with the company's bankers, who said they would welcome new ownership, although they pointed out that Alghanims were pretty dubious about its prospects. Not only was the company failing, it also had debts of £30,000. Anderson, having gained an assurance from Flack that he would do everything in his power to make Portman a success for Motherwell Bridge, made an offer of £5,000 for immediate acceptance. By close of business that day, he had in his hands the signed share transfer and Alghanim his £5,000. Portman Travel was officially a wholly owned Motherwell Bridge company.

In such manner, Motherwell Bridge made the most successful acquisition in its history. For almost 30 years the Group traded Portman Travel, helping a livewire management team to grow it through acquisition. In not one of those years did the company fail to return a solid profit. It became a major contributor to the company coffers, and a mainstay of income in the leaner financial years. When the time came to sell the travel company in 1996 in an institutional buy-out the sale realised £21.4 million, and at a single stroke increased Group reserves by 50 per cent. It took Motherwell Bridge back virtually to nil borrowings and gave it a strong financial springboard for further major acquisitions in engineering fields. It was undoubtedly one of the greatest success stories in the company's history.

Back in 1967, however, the purchase of Portman Travel was viewed with less equanimity. Director and company secretary Forbes D. Masterton, in particular, was outraged that a junior director (Anderson had only recently been appointed to the main Board) and an assistant company secretary should have unilaterally purchased a company which was patently well outside the Group's normal range of business interests. Motherwell Bridge had no experience in the travel trade. Masterton was equally affronted that the Board had not been consulted before the Group had been committed to the purchase - and wrote a number of blistering letters to the principals on the subject. Anderson received what amounted to an official reprimand.

Tiring of the blood being spilt over the Boardroom carpet over the affair, Anderson offered to personally buy back the company for £5,000. But Ronald Miller, who was more than a little amused at the in-fighting over what was really a very minimal cost Group purchase, and who personally considered it an excellent buy, cannily turned him down. Three years later Anderson again offered to buy Portman, this time for £28,000. Once again Ronald Miller, uninterested in even a 500 per cent profit on the Group's original investment, refused. Perhaps he had a strong premonition that from little

**PORTMAN TRAVEL** The original office and travel shop at 4 Portman Square, London, which is directly behind Selfridges Store on Oxford Street.

acorns mighty oaks might grow. Whatever the reason for his refusal to sell, grow Portman Travel most certainly did. Under the management of Norman Flack, the company performed steadily right through the 1970s.

Its most active period of expansion came about in the 1980s when Norman was joined in the business by his son, Graham, a chartered accountant, who was keen to build the business to a much greater size. In a decade when the travel trade was undergoing one of its periodic upheavals, Portman Travel embarked on growth by acquisition. Over a ten-year period, through a series of highly successful take-overs, father and son built up its annual turnover to around £60 million before making the quantum leap to a £100 million company by purchasing AA Travel at the beginning of the 1990s. Overnight, Portman doubled its outlets - the most important growth factor - and boosted staff levels to 350.

The key to Portman Travel's successful expansion was good management. The years of acquisition had brought with them a steady stream of excellent and experienced executives who blended into a first-class team, a fairly unusual phenomenon in take-overs, where clashes of business cultures (not to mention egos) usually result in fairly speedy departures. Portman Travel's four top executives all came from different acquisitions, which Group chief executive John Lumsden describes as "very unusual."

"We got a mature and experienced management of a younger age group," he says. "They blended very well. That was the real secret of Portman's success."

It was very largely a problem-free acquisition. As the Group executive who handled the Motherwell Bridge end of Portman's expansion plans, in consultation with the Flacks, John Lumsden found its affairs made only a small inroad on his time. However, all good things come to an end. For some time Motherwell Bridge had realised that owning a business travel agency did not sit particularly well in the Group portfolio. "We were an engineering group and it was a difficult one to explain to the shareholders," said Lumsden. "They could rightly have asked the question: If we were so good at business travel why didn't we become 100 per cent business travel? We had decided to exit at some point because it wasn't engineering."

There was another reason, too, why Motherwell Bridge felt the time to sell had arrived. As a £100 million company Portman Travel was denied the luxury of standing still. Major business clients like the comfort factor of dealing with large organisations. Without further acquisitions, there was a danger that Portman might not attract the volume of corporate business it was seeking. Future profitability was strongly linked to further expansion. Following the AA Travel acquisition, the company required to embark upon much greater acquisition spends to take it up the next rung of the ladder. "Up until that point, Portman Travel had not used much of our funds," said Lumsden. "But when we sat down and projected its ambitions it was going to demand a lot more funding than we as a Group were able to allocate without starving engineering."

In 1996, when the travel market was at a high, Motherwell Bridge sold off Portman Travel in a carefully structured institutional buy-out which kept on board the company's strong management team. "We were very careful that the management was kept in the picture throughout. With travel, goodwill is crucial. It can very easily walk out the door, so the management team were party to everything. They were well looked after," said Lumsden.

The sale brought to an end Motherwell Bridge's long, if somewhat unexpected, association with business travel. The profits so shrewdly accrued year on year, in fair weather and foul, were a steady and truly handsome contribution to the Group's financial position. In the run-up to the millennium, its sale was the icing on the cake.

From 1898 to 1998 is a long way for any organisation to travel. In a world of accelerated change, where many of the old trading certainties have vanished as developing countries have built up their own indigenous engineering industries, often in ultra-competitive low wage economies, Motherwell Bridge has successfully made the journey towards the next millennium because of a willingness to change and adapt. It has both specialised and diversified.

Only when one looks back over the route the century has taken Motherwell Bridge can the pattern be seen more clearly. Beyond its solid base of technological and engineering skills, there are several key features in its successful growth which have not yet been touched upon or are deserving of recognition.

First and foremost, Motherwell Bridge is a problem-solving company. It has always had the courage to face its times of adversity square-on. The reader may well ask: Do not all companies do that? The answer is No. A surprisingly large number of organisations embark upon half solutions and half measures, which in the end avail them nothing. It is the successful companies which respond directly and vigorously to challenge.

RIGHT: Neil Dougan, general manager of Motherwell Bridge Projects and Louis Casely-Hayford, chief executive of Volta River Authority co-signing the contract for the refurbishment of the 30-megawatt diesel generating station in Tema, Ghana.

BELOW: REACTOR VESSEL. Motherwell Bridge fabricated this reactor vessel being manoeuvred onto a roll-on/roll-off vessel at their Clydeside facility for delivery to Dow Chemicals at Barry, in South Wales.

**WICK AND THURSO GAS SATELLITE STATION.**
Vaporisers to change locally stored liquefied natural gas to
ambient temperature gas for domestic use.

**DAIRY AUTOMATION.** Bar-coding and automated warehouse
management system for Kiwi Cooperative Dairies Limited, the
second largest dairy company in New Zealand.

Secondly, for much of the last 20 years Motherwell
Bridge, although a family business, has always thought
big, acting very much like a plc in its corporate thinking
and goals. These days it is comfortable - and skilled - in
growth by acquisition.

Not being a publicly listed company with access to large
amounts of shareholders' capital, of necessity, its
acquisitions have tended to be smaller in size; it has
shopped around carefully.

The third long-running strand in its growth is an
excellent record of assimilation without disruption -
a lesson it learned the hard way during the Hunterston
years and its aftermath. Unlike many contemporary
businesses, Motherwell Bridge by and large absorbs new
companies into its operations without having to resort
to large-scale management clear-outs. Through regular
acquisitions and sympathetic rationalisations, there is a
constant flow of new business, new blood and new ideas
coming into the organisation. Having been accomplished
largely without tears, it breeds strong company loyalty.
It is a fact that Motherwell Bridge has one of the most
stable, and long-serving, corps of key personnel in industry.

No history of Motherwell Bridge would be complete
without having at least a peek into the future and what
the next century might have in store for the company.
In 1899, having awarded its shareholder directors a

5 per cent dividend on paid up capital, Motherwell
Bridge stepped into the 20th century with the princely
sum of £481 7s 3d (£481.36p) in the bank. When it
steps into the 21st century it is going to do a little
better. On a Group turnover of £208 million,
Motherwell Bridge's last published pre-tax profits (for
1996) were the highest in history, a record
£13,392,000, boosted by the gain on the Group's
disposal of its travel interests. Its bank borrowings were
minimal and its financial reserves at an all-time high.

Motherwell Bridge prepares for a new millennium in
fine financial shape, cash rich and in search of at least
one major new acquisition to grow the company. There
is a strong probability, too, that in the reasonably near
future the Group will become a fully listed plc on the
Stock Exchange - a logical extension to its current
activities. Although a private company, it has been
conducting its business very much like a plc for many
years. Successful flotation, if it is embarked upon, will
bring with it a whole raft of opportunities and challenges.

For Motherwell Bridge, the millennium is set to launch
it on a brand new and exciting chapter of one of the
great, and longest running engineering success stories
of Scotland. Once again the venerable, old dog which
in 100 years has contributed so mightily to landmark
engineering developments in Scotland and abroad, is
preparing to go out into the world and learn new tricks.

# Motherwell Bridge
# Scrapbook

ABOVE LEFT: The Duke of Kent visited the Motherwell Bridge stand at the 'Energy China' exhibition in March 1979. This trade fair attracted 700 British participants immediately after the People's Republic of China created its 'open door' policy. John Crawford is on the right explaining the company's manufacturing capabilities to the Duke, with John Moreland looking on.

ABOVE RIGHT: In 1967, the then Foreign Secretary, George Brown, visited Motherwell Bridge where he toured the works, speaking to many of the men and examining work in progress, much of which was destined for overseas markets. Here he is seen with (left) W. Law (foreman) and (middle) D. Nichols (progressman).

BELOW: In July 1974, the Queen and the Duke of Edinburgh visited the Linwood Incinerator near Glasgow Airport which was designed and built by Motherwell Bridge. On the left in the line-up is John Crawford and on the right is Dennis Eaton.

ABOVE: The Prince and Princess of Wales visited the Motherwell Bridge stand at the British Trade Fair in Oporto, Portugal, in February 1987. Motherwell Bridge's Jim Caldwell (right) and George Wycherley (2nd from right) discuss the merits of LPG as a fuel. In the foreground is a 'cut-away' exhibit of a 600 kg LPG vessel of the type produced in Motherwell.

BELOW LEFT: Charlie McNeilly (left), Motherwell Bridge's technical services manager shows visitors around the metallurgical laboratory at Motherwell Bridge. Mr K.B. Asante, High Commissioner for Ghana (right), Mrs Asante and Mr Anaman visited the company in May 1992.

BELOW RIGHT: The then Prime Minister, John Major, toured the Motherwell Bridge Works in February 1994. Here, accompanied by John Crawford, he greets some of the company's female staff.

The author would like to acknowledge the contribution made by the following:

**Ian Ballantyne**

**Cumbernauld Heritage Centre**

**Motherwell Football Club**

**Motherwell Heritage Centre**

**Motherwell Times**